Goats, Rabbits & Chickens

by
Hollis Lee

Countryside
Books

Preface

If you own a few acres or plan to acquire a country place, you probably know about the rich rewards associated with country living: the open space, the fresh air, the chance to do some real farming, gardening and animal raising on your own land.

*We have published this series of **Country Home & Small Farm Guides** to provide the basics you'll need to succeed in a broad range of projects and activities on two acres or 100.*

We realize that for most people country living is a very private pursuit. After all, a big part of its appeal is not having to look into the next guy's window when you look out of yours. But we hope you will communicate with us. Tell us how you like our books, share bits of country wisdom and suggest additional subjects or services we can provide.

Contents

Illustrations by Wayne Kibar

ISBN 0-88453-028-0

©1978 by Countryside Books
A.B. Morse Company, 200 James Street, Barrington, IL 60010

Printed in U.S.A.

Introduction

Goats, rabbits and chickens are ideally suited for the country place because all three can be raised to meet just your family's needs or to compete in a commercial market. You can even start out small, see how you feel, and enlarge your operation later if you wish.

This book is written for the novice farmer — for the person who needs to know what's involved in the venture. The information on selecting stock, housing and equipment, feeding, preparing the products, controlling disease, and breeding should not only help you decide what's involved, but also tell you how to proceed.

Good luck!

4

GOATS

The dairy goat is ideally adapted to the country place. No domesticated animal has a wider range of usefulness. With little care, she can be as profitable as a dozen laying hens. As a provider of household milk and meat, the goat can fulfill her function under a

5

wide range of conditions. In fact, you can select stock that is compatible with your facilities and terrain — and the goat produces equally well in hot, arid regions and cold, wet regions.

In addition to the sterling qualities mentioned above, the milk goat can stand on two rocks of virtue — its excellent milk and its exceptional feeding habits and digestive capacity. The goat has long been known as "the poor man's cow," an honorable title that is well-deserved. However, the techniques and problems in keeping a goat are so much less than those in keeping a cow that there really isn't any comparison. Their milk is so similar that most people can't tell the difference; among those who can, most prefer goat's milk. Because the goat can live on terrain that can't support other livestock, it is an easy animal to feed.

With all of these admirable characteristics, surely you should consider having a milk goat on your country place. Read on to learn just how easy it is.

Selecting the Stock

Milk Producers

The main considerations in selecting stock for milk production are inherent milking capacity, food intake capacity, and food-to-milk conversion efficiency. The pedigree breeder aims to produce an animal with all these qualities developed as highly as possible. But the degree to which you need goats with each of these distinct qualities will depend upon the system under which you manage them. Three main management systems are described below.

Stall feeding or yarding

Under this system, the goats have most of their feed cut and carried to them. Labor is the biggest cost with feed a close second. The type of goat you need is one that will produce the maximum amount of milk for the minimum feed. For that reason, you do not want a goat with a big feed intake capacity. Even though the modern dairy goat is able to consume a prodigious daily ration of cheap roughage and convert it into milk, you will need to provide a generous measure of concentrates. Roughage that is cheap on the ground where it grows becomes more expensive every time it is handled.

Feeding on improved land

On improved land you need quite another kind of goat — one with as high a milking potential as possible and a good feed intake capacity. The more forage crops she eats, the less expensive concentrates she will need.

Goats grazing improved land need a little fat or a coat of long hair. The udder should be exceptionally well hung, broad in the base, and close to the body. The weight of a big udder, a well-filled and capacious paunch, and a rather fat body are more easily carried on short sturdy legs. Ground clearance for the udder is of little importance in cultivated fields. The leading breeders produce excellent stock for this purpose.

Free range on scrub and rough grazing

This management system requires goats that obtain the bulk of their ration foraging on rough grazing areas. Big feed capacity is of prime importance. These goats consume ample fiber to keep them warm and have no need for fat or long hair; therefore, their feed-to-milk conversion efficiency may be very high and their cost is next to nothing. You don't need a goat with a great milking capacity because any advantage from a super yield will be more than cancelled out by the large requirement for concentrates to maintain it. The goat will need long legs to give the udder clearance and to make foraging among trees and brush possible.

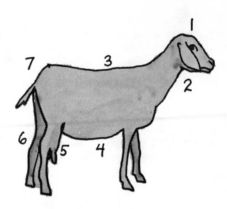

The Unproductive Goat Profile

1. Has a short, convex face and a more-or-less upturned nose.
2. A short, coarse neck.
3. Shallow, straight ribs and a brick shape profile.
4. A small belly.
5. Small, tough-skinned vessels, purse shaped with finger-breadth teats.
6. Her hocks nearly knock together as she walks.
7. Her rump is short and steep.

Meat Producers

In considering the goat as a meat producer, you should differentiate between kid meat and goat meat. Kid meat, a by-product of the dairy goat, can be both delicious and nutritious when handled correctly. It is every bit as good as veal and rather more versatile in the hands of a good cook.

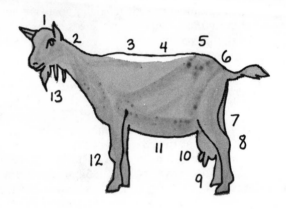

Profile of a Productive Dairy Goat

1. Long lean head, with lively expression.
2. Long lean silky-skinned neck.
3. Strong, straight back.
4. Deep, wide sprung rib cage, the last rib curving back.
5. The hollow in front of the hips.
6. The long, gently sloping rump.
7. The capacious udder.
8. The hocks straight to avoid damage to udder.
9. The teats are hand size.
10. Extension of udder forward.
11. Under the belly you can feel the knobby milk veins.
12. Strong, straight front legs.
13. Long, powerful jaw.

Housing and Equipment

The housing and equipment needs for dairy goats are not very extensive. Fencing, a running tether, simple sheds, and some handling equipment are all that you will need.

Fencing

One of the biggest problems you will have with goats is maintaining control. The goat's ability to destroy the standard stock fence, flowers, gardens and crops is notorious. Because country places often are in built-up areas, you should construct a fence as much to keep the dogs out as the goats in. For these purposes, you will find special woven-wire fencing best. The minimum height should be 5 feet — a 4 foot woven wire with 3 barbed wire strands on top. Space the posts close together so the wire won't sag. Some types of brush goats can stand flat-footed and jump clear of a 5 foot-fence, but most dairy goats will be safely contained, especially if there is adequate forage available.

Running Tether

If you want your goats to graze in special areas outside their normal pasture, you can control them by making any one of the following running tethers.

Single running tether

Combine a fairly short length of chain, not more than 3 feet and not less than 18 inches, with a swivel ring. Slip the ring around a wire before you stretch it taut along the ground. This will permit the goat to range within that area. If you use a short wire, attach the ends of the wire to two stakes, the heads of which are driven flush with the ground. If the wire is long, stretch it taut between two posts set firmly in the ground.

Multiple running tether

If you want more than one goat tethered to the same wire, drive stakes into the ground at intervals, and staple the wire to them. This will divide the wire into sections and allow you to accommodate more than one goat.

Picket tether

This is the most common type of tethering. The goat is fitted with a collar and chained to a stake driven in the ground. This tether is almost always used to graze a billy goat, as the male is kept segregated except during the breeding season. For anyone who is not a pedigree breeder of the first class, there is no purpose served in rearing male kids for anything except meat. Those who care to

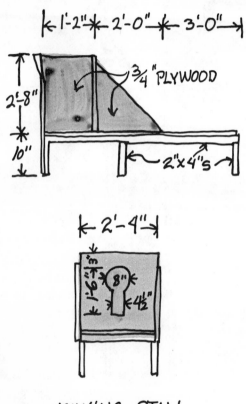

MILKING STALL
FOR
GOATS

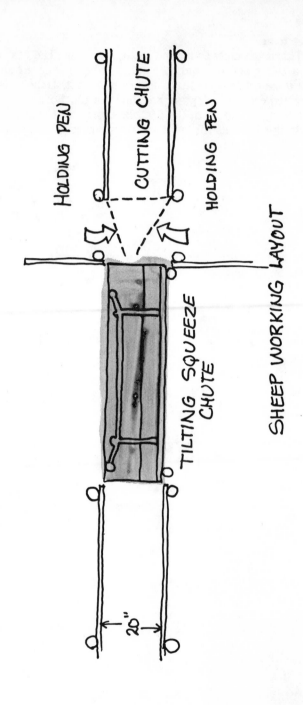

HOLDING PEN

CUTTING CHUTE

HOLDING PEN

TILTING SQUEEZE CHUTE

20"

SHEEP WORKING LAYOUT

12

disregard this advice must accept the consequences of a very troublesome task of control.

Stalls and Bins

Milk goats are much more content if they have their own stalls and feed bins. If possible, build a small stall on a raised platform to make milking easier. The stall should be sheltered from the weather with local climate conditions determining which type of stall is best. Hay racks and water troughs should be 8 to 12 inches above the ground. Hay and grain storage facilities should be incorporated into the shelter's design.

Loading Chute

A small loading chute is needed to load and unload the animals. In addition, working the animals will be much easier if a *tilting squeeze chute* is available to do foot trimming, artificial insemination and pregnancy diagnosis.

Feeding

What and how much you feed a goat depends upon its food capacity and *food conversion efficiency,* and the kind of pasture and rations you have.

Food Capacity

The goat's food capacity is largely a matter of sheer size, with particular emphasis on the depth, width, and spread of ribs and the development of a deep, wedge-shaped profile. However, a nervous fidgety goat eats more than a placid one. A long jaw is a help to a big appetite, and long legs are necessary to reach high brush.

Most goats that sag in the middle cannot carry a great load of fodder over rough grazing. The Nubian breed has legs more widely set than other breeds and, like a suspension bridge, Nubians are built to sag.

Food Conversion Efficiency

Food *conversion efficiency* can be measured by the eye. Generally a short, fat goat will be a low milk producer and a long, lean, glossy goat will be a high milk producer. All goats carry fat in their chests and over their bellies. If you find fat on the back and rump of the milker, the milk bucket is being short changed to put on fat. On a young goatling, the fat on the back is a reserve for its first lactation.

Feed and Rations

The goat is able to consume the fibrous foods its vast capacity enables it to utilize. The goat needs and possesses the toughest mouth of all the *ruminants.* This remarkable organ is the goat's passport to a world of well-protected vegetable treasures such as nettles, briars, and brambles — and the nutritive ration of white clover is at its best. Not only can goats live where cattle and sheep would starve, they can also share a pasture with cattle and sheep and help improve the pasture by eating the brambles, weeds and scrub. On better pasture, the goat is capable of converting fodder into milk as efficiently as the best strains of dairy cattle. On the country place, the milk supply can be produced much cheaper with goats than with cows and with a lot less trouble.

If you decide to feed your goats rations, you can give them a specially prepared milk goat ration from the local feed supply house. You can also provide a farm mix of 1/3 cottonseed meal or soybean meal, 1/3 cracked corn or milo, and 1/3 whole oats. The goat should have access to salt and minerals at free choice and have plenty of clean water.

Goat Products

Goat Milk

Advantages

The quality of goat's milk is excellent. When its composition is compared with that of cow's milk, there is really very little difference, with the edge going to the goat. Of 3000 people from various walks of life who sampled goat's milk at a recent dairy show, only three thought it tasted "peculiar"; the majority were pleasantly surprised. A slight preference was shown for goat's milk when drunk after a sample of cow's milk.

The idea that goat's milk tastes peculiar probably came about as a result of the stink of the male. Female goats do not stink. When the billy is separated from the milking goats, the stink of the male cannot taint the milk. It is better not to keep the billy, but to pay a fee to utilize the services when needed.

Goat's milk possesses certain nutritive qualities listed below that cow's milk lacks.

1. Goat's milk will beneficially replace cow's milk in the diet of those people who suffer from allergy to cow's proteins.
2. The proteins of goat's milk are more easily digested by most infants and some adults.
3. The fat content of goat's milk is more easily digested than the fat content of cow's milk.
4. The all-around digestibility of goat's milk, associated with the fact that it is mildly laxative and 50% richer in vitamin B1, gives it a marked superiority.
5. The higher buffering qualities of goat's milk enhance its value for sufferers from peptic ulcers and other digestive disorders that call for treatment with antacid drugs.
6. The high proportion of butterfat gives goat's milk a greater energy value per unit volume than cow's milk. The size of fat globules makes the goat's milk easy to digest, has a bearing on its value in cheese and ice cream, and accounts for some difficulties in the mechanical separation of goat's cream.

Procedures

Many goat keepers are poor milkers. A novice may be well advised to follow this procedure. Be sure to milk the goat consistently from only one side. Don't milk the goat from behind.

1. Grasp a teat lightly in one hand.
2. Press the hand gently upwards toward the base of the udder in order to fill the teat with milk.
3. Close the index finger tightly around the neck of the teat with the hand pressing gently upwards.
4. Close the other fingers in succession tightly around the teat to force the milk down and out.
5. Keep repeating the procedure until the udder is milked completely dry.
6. If the goat has short teats, use only one finger and the thumb. Hold the teat between the index finger and the knuckle of the thumb. Rotate your hand up and down from the wrist in a pumping motion as your hands move down the teat. Keep pressure against the thumb.

If more milk is produced than you can consume, try to separate the cream and feed the skim milk to pigs and chickens. You can use the cream as sour cream or whipping cream. You can churn butter, but it is not on a par with butter made from cow's milk. The finest cheeses are also made from goat's milk.

Cleanliness

Whether the end product of the goat dairy is fresh milk, cream, butter or cheese, a prime requirement is cleanliness. In trying to maintain cleanliness, goats offer two advantages and two disadvantages. The advantages are that goat's milk naturally has a lower bacterial count, and chemicals can be used to sterilize goat dairy equipment. One disadvantage is that goat dung is exceedingly dry and dusty, and therefore difficult to keep from becoming airborne and settling in the milk pail. Also, the goat's need for a warm bed and freedom makes it impossible to achieve a clinical cleanliness.

To keep the milk as clean as possible, brush the goat down and wash the udder before milking. Use a hooded milk pail. Keep the milking stand and the barn as clean as possible. Some milking machines on the market can be adapted for the dairy goat, but they can only be justified if you are producing for the commercial market.

Goat Meat

Raising goats for meat

Kid meat production brings one new consideration into goat-keeping practices — you will have to castrate the male kid within 2 or 3 weeks after birth. The effect of castration on the growth rate of male kids is far greater than on ram lambs and bull calves. Because the male kid may be sexually mature at 3 months, the effect of castration at birth may double the efficiency with which the kid converts milk into meat and causes the milk to be better.

The simple and safe way to castrate is to use an "elastrator." This is a specially designed rubber band that cuts off the supply of blood to the scrotum. However, a sterile knife is quick and easy to use. The kid will bleed a little, so you will need to watch for any infection.

Procedures

Use the following procedures to prepare the kid goat meat.

1. The most convenient way to kill the kid is to shoot it with a .22 rifle.
2. Hang the kid by the hind legs and bleed it by cutting its throat.
3. Skin the goat while the body is still warm. The ligaments attaching the skin to the body are strong and if left until cold, the skin is extremely difficult to remove.
4. With a sharp knife make a single, clean, light cut from a central point between the two teats to the skin above the breast bone.
5. From the same point make a cut to the skin above the first joint of the hind legs.
6. Loosen the skin from the belly and thighs by using your fingers and a small wooden spoon or wooden paddle. Do not use a knife.
7. Then, continue on the legs to a point above the hooves.
8. Loosen the skin around the anus and vulva. Cut around these openings and tie them tightly with a strong string.
9. Cut a slit on the center of the tail and peel the skin.
10. Next, loosen and peel the skin from flanks and back, using the paddle or spoon to loosen the skin right up to the front of the chest. Be sure to keep the hair side rolled under to prevent it from touching the carcass.
11. Continue the first belly cut to the throat and work skin carefully from the chest.

12. Remove the head.
13. Cut a slit up to the first joints of the front legs and strip them.
14. To dress out the carcass, cut around the anus and vulva that were previously tied and continue with a slit to the chest.
15. Next, split the rib cage down the center with a heavy knife or hatchet. Remove the internal organs.
16. Allow the carcass to hang in a cool place until the meat has become firm before cutting it up.

As far as utilizing the meat from an old goat, forget it. Don't waste time with it unless it is prepared for dog or cat food.

Breeding

The goat's natural breeding season is in October and November. Since the goat carries her young for five months, this has the young arriving in the spring months of April and May, a time when fresh green grazing is available to insure a bountiful supply of milk for the welcome newcomers. The problem of winter milk supply is solved by allowing the goat to "run through" alternate years and run a 22 month lactation.

There is no technical difficulty involved in artificial insemination of goats. *Artificial insemination* can eliminate the need for keeping the male goat. The services of a veterinarian and the cost of semen will not be as much as the cost of feeding and caring for a billy. You also won't have to cope with the smell of the billy, which can become a real problem and tends to be overlooked. If clothing contaminated by the billy's stink comes into contact with an open pail of milk, it can cause the milk to have an off flavor.

Breeds

Although the vast majority of goats are mixed breeds, there are a few recognized breeds in this country. These breeds do have distinctive utility characteristics, but it is hard to find stock that has reasonable uniformity within the chosen breed. Select the strains and individuals to conform to your purposes. Some of the characteristics, such as udder shape, long legs, coat quality and degree of fat, declare themselves openly to the eye and touch. To discern the hidden qualities that make a good milker is difficult, but if good milking capacity is what you want, look for a long lean head, interested eyes, lively movements, a long slim neck and a gentle sloping rump. Feel for a fine pliable skin with a smooth and lustrous coat, for a large elastic udder and knobby milk veins. If possible, consult milk records of the goat, or her dam and sire's dam.

The breeds described below are most common recognized breeds.

Anglo-Nubian

The Anglo-Nubian is of mixed origin. It is the most distinctive of our recognized breeds both in appearance and performance. Colors vary with roan and white predominating. Lop ears and Roman nose are typical. It is more heavy-fleshed than the Swiss breeds, weighing about 150 pounds. This goat gives milk yields up to 300 gallons per year with about 5 percent butterfat. The milk contains about 10 to 11 percent solids as compared to 8 to 9 percent for other breeds. This makes it a producer of what is perhaps the most highly digestible and perfectly balanced food available to mankind.

Nubian

The udder of the Nubian, although not remarkable for its shapliness, has good ground clearance. It undoubtedly produces the most desirable of all milk. Its hair is short, but it has a layer of fat that enables it to withstand adverse weather. The Nubian makes a good nurse animal for raising calves. The milk is also good for raising pigs and chickens. The one disadvantage is that the nanny Nubian goat can become exceptionally vocal at times.

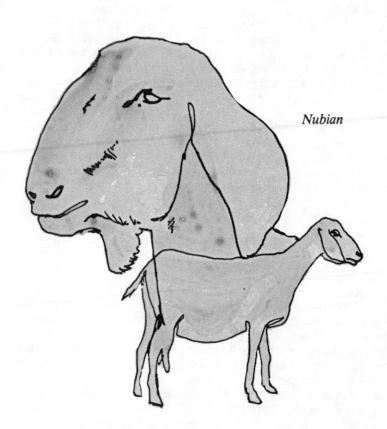

Nubian

22

Saanen

The Saanen is nominally of Swiss origin, white in color, placid in disposition, rather short in the leg, and capable of the very highest yields. This breed is well suited for improved land. Udders of this breed are well shaped and well hung. Some produce as much as 300 gallons of milk a year with around 4 percent butterfat.

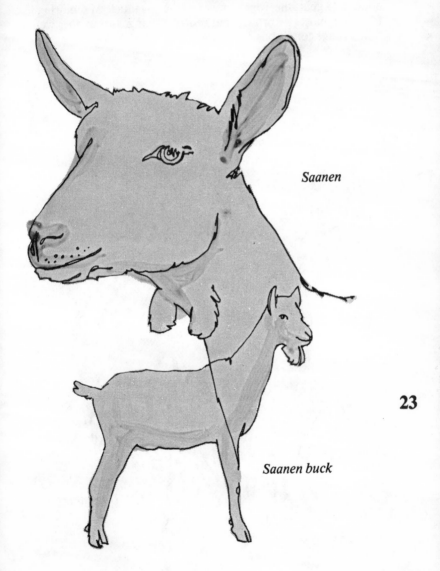

Saanen

23

Saanen buck

Toggenburg

The Toggenburg is descended from Swiss stock, is brown and white, and has an active but affectionate disposition. The Toggenburg is a small goat, usually under 100 pounds adult weight. The udder is well hung. Milk seldom exceeds 200 gallons per year, with butterfat percentage low (under 3 percent). As a stall-fed household goat, the Toggenburg has the advantage of requiring less feed than most. Its brown coat resists staining. It also does well on rough range conditions.

24

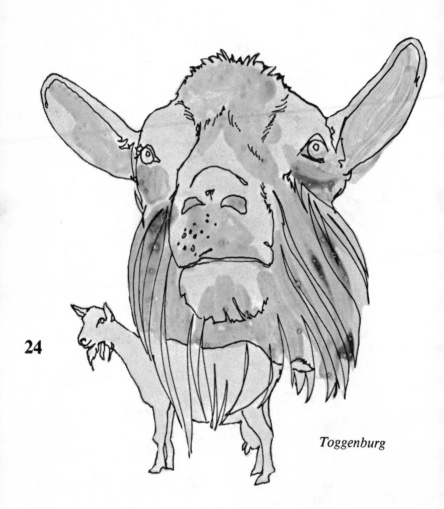

Toggenburg

Alpine

The Alpine, black and white in color, is a big leggy goat capable of high yields of milk with 4 percent butterfat. It is probably the most adaptable all-around breed and can be developed into a first rate goat for scrub and brush ranges.

25

Alpine

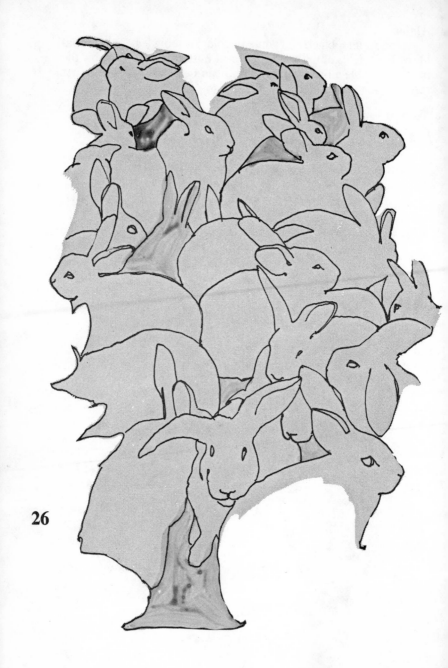

RABBITS

Domestic rabbits used to be kept primarily as pets in the United States, but in more recent years they have become increasingly popular for their meat. The taste of fried rabbit is not unlike that of chicken, and some people actually prefer rabbit to chicken. It is also delicious fricasseed, and rabbit stewed with prunes is out of this world.

One reason for the increased interest in raising rabbits for meat is that they can convert feed (primarily grain) into meat at a better ratio than any other animal except chickens. Properly fed with a well-balanced ration, rabbits can produce one pound of meat for every four pounds or less of feed consumed.

The production of rabbits is a natural for the country place. It is ideally suited because it requires very little land, and a comparatively small outlay of labor, equipment and capital.

Be careful when you handle rabbits because they are easily injured. The right way to handle a rabbit is to grasp the loose skin over the shoulders with one hand while placing the other hand under the hind quarters, allowing most of the weight of the rabbit to rest on this hand. Young fryers can be handled without damage by placing either hand right in front of the hind quarters and lifting gently, allowing the head to hang down. Carrying boxes are the most convenient way to move rabbits from one location to another. Less damage is likely to occur to the rabbit, and the handler is less likely to get scratched. Rabbits may be seriously injured if caught or lifted by the ears.

Selecting the Stock

Choosing a breed and selecting the starting stock are some of the first decisions you will have to make. Assuming you are new to rabbit production, start on a small scale until you have developed the skills and knowledge necessary to successfully expand the operation.

The success of the venture will depend to a large degree on the selection of the starting stock you purchase. Select rabbits of good quality and representative of the breed. They should have erect ears, bright eyes, and straight and shapely tails and feet. It is very important that they be free of diseases. Try to purchase the stock from local sources if at all possible and from breeders who keep records. By checking the records, the rabbits' performance can be determined, including size of litters produced each year, rate of growth, and freedom from diseases. Examine the rabbits carefully; don't buy a "pig in a poke." Profit is the ultimate goal, so give careful consideration to potential litter sizes. A profitable doe should have 7 to 10 young at least 4 times a year. The doe should produce litters that weigh 5½ pounds in 3 weeks, and each of the young should weigh 4 pounds at weaning age in 8 weeks. A doe of this caliber gives a good return on the investment.

In the beginning you might want to buy the does already bred. This is an especially good idea if you don't know which breed you want. Buying a bred doe from three or four different breeds will help you determine the merits of each.

If you want to pursue your own breeding program, three or four does and one buck will be ample to get you started in the business. Once the does reach breeding age, the business will expand in a hurry. The experience you gain by raising your own does will probably offset any losses you incur because of lack of knowledge. However, once people decide to raise rabbits, they usually don't want to wait the time required to grow a doe to breeding age. Whichever way you decide to proceed, go ahead and give it a whirl. Just keep the initial operation small. If problems arise, seek advice from growers in the area, from feed companies, the county agent, and books and magazines.

Three primary markets are normally available for marketing rabbits: (1) meat, (2) furs and (3) laboratory animals. There are also three secondary markets that may provide a reasonably good outlet: (1) selling the rabbits for pets, (2) selling breeding stock to other growers, and (3) selling rabbits to young people for 4H and FFA projects.

The most receptive market will be the one for meat. The rabbits may be sold to processors, who will do their own slaughtering, processing and distribution, or you can process them yourself and sell them directly to individuals in your area, supermarkets and restaurants. If you use the latter method to market part or all of your rabbits, check with the County Health Department concerning regulations governing slaughtering operations.

There are breeds available that are capable of fulfilling all of the requirements referred to above, including American, Californian, Flemish Giant, French Silver, New Zealand and Checkered Giant. Other breeds are also satisfactory, but fancy or single-purpose breeds are not recommended unless they are raised strictly for show animals. In the final analysis, however, the breed(s) you select will probably reflect your personal preference.

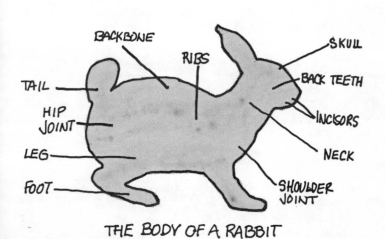

THE BODY OF A RABBIT

Housing

The housing for rabbits is simple in design and construction. The main purpose of the housing is to protect the rabbits from wind, rain, and bright sunlight. Rabbits will suffer from extreme heat, especially does that are pregnant or with newborn litters. Shelters must be well ventilated, dry and able to protect the rabbits from getting wet. Damp, matted fur promotes disease and respiratory problems.

In areas where the climate is mild, the hutches can be set outside under trees or under some other type of shade such as a lath house. If the temperature drops below 20°F, the rabbits will need additional protection from the cold.

If you use an open shed, equip it with panels that can be put up in colder weather to furnish a wind break. Enclose the area around the rabbit hutches with a good, tight fence that will keep out dogs, cats and wild animals.

Regardless of the size of the operation in the beginning, make allowances for later expansion. It seems that no one starting in the rabbit business stays at a constant level of production — they either give up or expand.

No type of shelter can be designed that will meet all conditions, but the saw tooth design offers many advantages. It is well suited for pole type construction, and it can be added to in almost all directions. It has good ventilation, and it offers good protection from the elements.

Hutches

Hutches used outside should be constructed with a solid, rainproof top and back side and should have panels or curtains. Because the front is normally constructed of wire mesh, curtains offer a method of protection during cold and stormy weather.

Hutches used inside buildings or under a roofed shelter are best made of all-wire construction. Several different types are available commercially and are well suited for this purpose. They are sanitary, easy to clean, require very little maintenance, and are economical to purchase. Plans and directions for constructing your own all-wire hutches are included in this section.

Size

Rabbits should be kept in individual hutches so they will have room in which to exercise. As a rule of thumb, the hutch size should equal one square foot for each pound of body weight. Limit the depth of the hutch to 2½ feet so that you can reach the back from the door. The normal height is 24 inches and the normal length 4 to 6 feet. Hutches can be tiered if space is limited, but it is not recommended unless absolutely necessary because it increases labor, spreads diseases more easily, and appears to reduce reproduction.

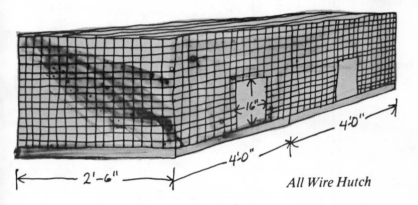

All Wire Hutch

Double all-wire hutch

A double all-wire hutch is best inside buildings or under a roofed shelter. Use the following procedure.

31

1. Start with a 1 inch x 1/2 inch mesh for the floor. Cut it to a dimension of 102 x 36 inches.
2. Turn up 3 inches on all four sides and wire the corners together.
3. Cut two pieces of 1 x 2-inch wire mesh that measure 48 x 78 inches.
4. Use a 2 x 4 wood block and a hammer to bend the wire upward 24 inches on either end of the 78-inch length.
5. Bend the other 78-inch length in the same manner. This forms the sides and tops of the hutches.

(Cont. on page 35.)

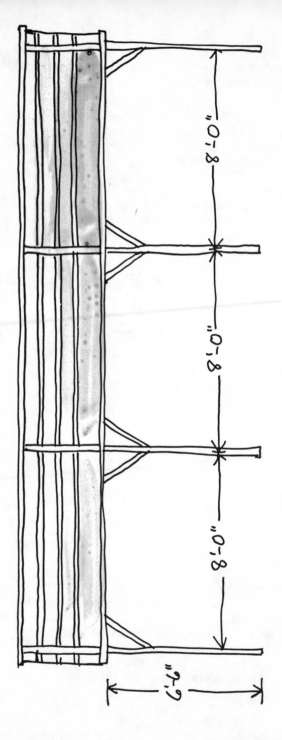

32

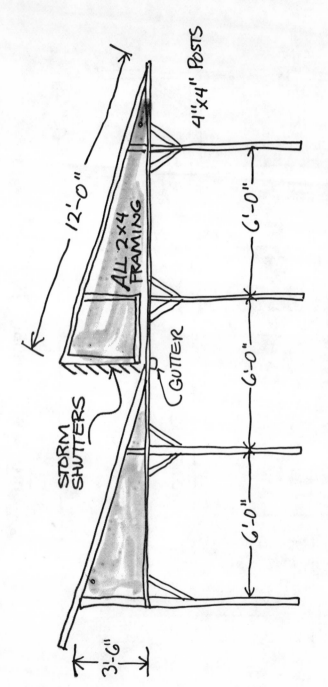

STORM SHUTTERS

GUTTER

12'-0"

ALL 2×4 FRAMING

4"×4" POSTS

6'-0"

6'-0"

6'-0"

3'-6"

SAW TOOTH RABBIT SHELTER

33

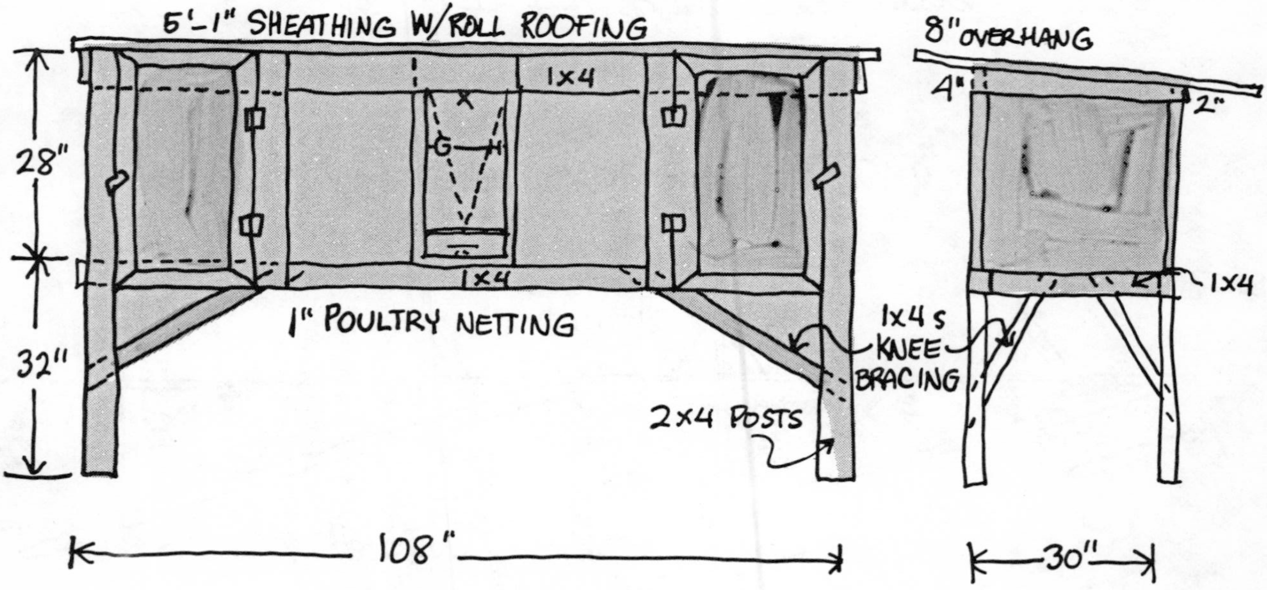

8" OVERHANG

2"

4"

1×4

30"

5'-1" SHEATHING W/ROLL ROOFING

1×4

1×4

1" POULTRY NETTING

1×4'S KNEE BRACING

2×4 POSTS

108"

28"

32"

34

TWO LIMIT RABBIT HUTCH

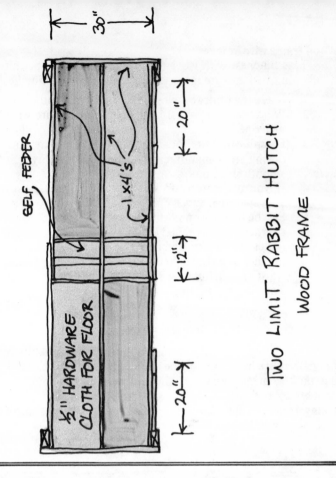

TWO LIMIT RABBIT HUTCH

WOOD FRAME

SELF FEEDER

1 x 4's

½" HARDWARE CLOTH FOR FLOOR

30"

20"

12"

20"

6. Drop the U sections into the bottom, and wire the bottom to the top with hen-cage clips. Be sure that all sharp ends of the wires are bent over out of the way.

7. Cut 3 pieces of 1 x 2-inch wire mesh that measure 24 x 30 inches, one for each end and one for the partition.

8. Put the end pieces in place and secure them with hen-cage clips.

9. Center the partition, and secure it in the same manner.

10. Cut doors in the front of the hutches that are at least 16 inches square. Use large hen-clips to make the door hinges.

11. Take two 9-foot lengths of 1/2-inch steel bars. Use hog rings to fasten the steel rods to the floor of the hutch both front and back. This will provide a way to suspend the hutches.

Wood frame wire hutches

These hutches, with woven wire sides and ends, permit good circulation of air and are more sanitary than all-wood hutches.

1. Make the floors of wire mesh or slatted wood.
2. Weld the mesh with 16 gauge galvanized wire with 1 x 2-inch openings.
3. Examine the wire for sharp points which sometimes occur during the manufacturing process. Always put the smooth side up.
4. If you use hardwood slats for the bottoms, use 1-inch slats spaced 5/8 inch apart.
5. Set the hutches on posts or suspend them with wires from overhead. Suspended hutches eliminate all supports under the hutches and make cleaning much easier. Set the hutches at a convenient height, usually slightly above the waist. Each hutch will require equipment for feeding, watering and nesting.

Nesting Boxes

The *nesting box* is important to raising young rabbits successfully. They are hung outside the hutch on the ends or back, depending on the arrangement of the hutches. They should be large enough to prevent crowding, but small enough to prevent the young from getting separated. If the young separate into two or

36

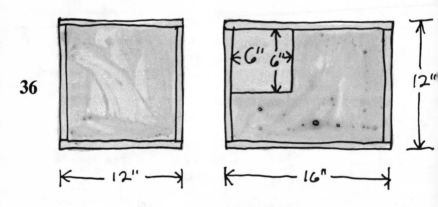

WOODEN RABBIT NEST BOX

more groups, the doe will only allow one group to nurse. The nesting boxes must have good ventilation and proper drainage.

Two types of nesting boxes are usually used. The box-type is fabricated from ½-inch plywood or 1 x 12s with a top and bottom that can be removed to facilitate cleaning. The nail keg nesting box is made from a wooden nail keg. Nail a 1 x 6 board about 14 inches long to each end of the keg to prevent it from rolling. Drill four 1-inch holes in the solid end of the keg to improve ventilation. Drill a 1/4-inch hole in the bottom for drainage.

Prefabricated nest boxes are available from many suppliers of small animal equipment. These suppliers are normally listed under laboratory animal equipment suppliers.

If additional protection is necessary to keep the young litter warm during cold weather, put the nesting box inside a larger box with insulation between the two. Be careful not to block off the vent holes completely.

Cooling Boxes

Use *cooling boxes* or baskets in the summer when the young become too hot in the nesting box. During the hot part of the day, place the young in the cooling box which is hung inside the hutch. Return the young to the nesting box at night. The cooling box should be about 12 inches square and covered with hardware cloth so the air can circulate through it.

Equipment

Feed Hopper

The feed hopper should be made from metal because rabbits will chew on wood. Also, wood is not as sanitary. A square, 5-gallon can is big enough to provide good-sized hoppers for self-feeding. Use the following procedure to make your feed hopper.

1. Cut off the top of the can.
2. Cut two openings in both the front and rear of the can. The openings should be 4 inches from the bottom, 4 inches high, and 3 inches wide.
3. Cut the openings 1/4 smaller all the way around so that the 1/4 inch can be turned under to provide a smooth rolled edge.
4. Make partitions from 1/4-inch or 3/8-inch plywood cut to divide the can into four compartments.
5. Cut two pieces of wood 30 inches long and 4½ inches

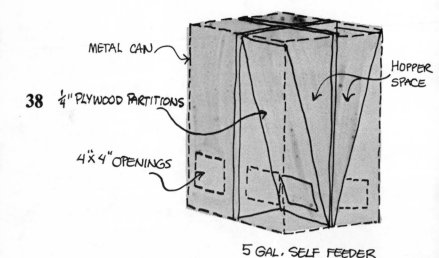

METAL CAN

HOPPER SPACE

38 ¼" PLYWOOD PARTITIONS

4"X 4" OPENINGS

5 GAL. SELF FEEDER

wide from 3/8-inch plywood. At one end, cut an opening 6 inches x 3½ inches.

6. Slide each piece of wood into a compartment with the opening to the bottom and resting against the partition. The top of the wood should rest against the outside wall of the top of the can.

7. The same system can be used for a self-feeder mounted on the outside of the hutch. If the feeder is attached to one hutch, cut only one opening in the side of the 5-gallon can. If you install it between two hutches, two openings will be necessary.

See the sketch for more detailed information.

Water Supply

Water is critical for rabbits and should be readily available.

Open crocks

Half-gallon water crocks are used by many rabbit breeders, but one-pound coffee cans are also used extensively. Coffee cans are normally attached to the hutch so that they cannot be turned over. The advantage of coffee cans is that in freezing weather the ice can be easily removed. Both the crocks and coffee cans require cleaning and refilling with water each day.

Automatic watering systems

Automatic watering systems have short nipples from which the rabbits suck the water as they want it. Rabbits adapt to the automatic watering system with very little trouble.

The automatic watering systems have proved very satisfactory, are inexpensive, and eliminate the time consuming chores of washing, disinfecting, rinsing and filling crocks or cans. Be sure to install the system in accordance with the manufacturer's recommendations. In all cases use a water pressure regulator in front of the system to reduce the pressure. In cold weather, the system can be protected from freezing with electrical heating tape wrapped around the pipe. The tape can be controlled with a thermostat set to come on just above freezing.

Glass bottle

A compromise between the automatic water system and the open crock method is a glass bottle with a special nipple from which the rabbit can drink. The glass bottle is mounted on the side of the hutch at a slight angle that puts the nipple inside the hutch. This system eliminates the rabbits' contaminating the water supply.

These water bottles and nipples are available from suppliers of small animal equipment.

Troughs and Hay Mangers

Troughs and hay mangers may be incorporated as part of the hutch if hay or home-grown grains are going to be fed as a part of the rations. Install guards over the feed troughs to prevent the rabbits from getting into the troughs and wasting feed.

Feeding

Types of Feed

More than 75% of the rabbits raised in the United States are now fed exclusively with commercially prepared feed. There are three basic types of commercial feeds on the market: (1) the all grain pellet, which must have a quantity of hay served with it to complete the diet requirements, (2) a complete ration pellet that has the hay requirements and all other nutritional requirements included, and (3) a complete ration which includes all the nutritional requirements, plus medication to control respiratory problems and coccidiosis. Beginners should feed the complete ration with medication because correct feeding is the most important factor in raising strong healthy litters. It will cost less than a nickel more to raise a rabbit to full maturity with medicated feed.

The commercial feeds are much easier to handle than your own mixtures. With proper feeders, waste is eliminated. Under some conditions, the savings gained from eliminating waste alone will pay for the additional cost needed to purchase pelleted commercial feeds.

As you gain experience feeding rabbits and if you have an abundance of home-grown grain and/or hay you might want to mix and feed your own ration. In any case, never make a sudden and complete change in the rabbits' rations. If you change, do it slowly over several days by adding a small amount of the new ration to the old. Increase the amount of new ration a little each day until the complete change has been accomplished.

Feed Requirements

The United States Department of Agriculture in its Farmers Bulletin No. 1730, "Rabbit Production" establishes two basic types of rations for rabbit production. Most commercial feed manufacturers prepare both type of rations.

Requirements for dry does, herd bucks, developing young

Content	% of ration
Protein	12 to 15
Fat	2 to 3.5
Fiber	20 to 27
Nitrogen-free Extract	43 to 47
Ash or Mineral	5 to 6.5

The dry does and herd bucks are normally hand-fed their rations each day to limit their intake. The developing young should have self-feeders with free choice to feed at all times. If this feed is not available, feed the higher protein feed described below to all classes of rabbits.

Requirements for pregnant or nursing does

Content	% of ration
Protein	16 to 20
Fat	3 to 5.5
Fiber	15 to 20
Nitrogen-free Extract	44 to 50
Ash or Mineral	4.5 to 6.5

Does that are pregnant or with litters should be fed free choice, and given all of the high protein ration they will eat. The day the doe kindles, cut her rations in half to prevent udder problems. On the third day, start increasing her ration a little at a time for the next week. After that, keep the feed before her at all times together with plenty of water. In warm weather, a doe and her litter can consume as much as one gallon of water in a 24 hour period.

If you have to feed dry does, herd bucks, or developing young this higher protein ration, feed them less than you would the lower protein ration. On the average, 4 pounds of commercial feed should produce one pound of meat. The higher protein feed will increase the cost slightly for developing young, but they may make the same weight on a little less feed to offset part of the cost.

Rabbits have a habit of reingesting matter that they excrete. This is material that has passed through their digestive tract that they pick up, chew and swallow. This is normal, and does not mean that anything is out of balance in their diet.

Store the feed in a clean, dry place. Never feed any feeds that show signs of being sour or contain mold or rotten particles. When you open commercial feed sacks, place the contents in either a plastic or steel trash can with a tight fitting cover. This serves a dual

42

purpose: It keeps the feed from rodents, and keeps the feed dry and free from contamination.

Schedules

Rabbits like to keep on a schedule. The number of times they are fed is not as important as the schedule. Try to establish a convenient schedule and stick to it. Rabbits east mostly at night; therefore, late afternoon feeding is considered to be a good time. Also, the rabbits are less likely to be disturbed at this time.

Rabbit Products

The most humane method of killing a rabbit is to hold the rabbit by its hind legs with one hand, place the thumb of the other hand on the neck behind the rabbit's ears, and with the forefinger extended under the chin, push down on the neck stretching the animal slightly until it is tense. Then, press down with the thumb, and snap the animal's head back with a quick movement. This will dislocate its neck, and the rabbit will not struggle. Another way to kill the rabbit is with a heavy blow at the base of the skull. This is also quick and easy, but not as humane.

Rabbit Skin

Use the following procedure to skin the rabbit and prepare the skin.

1. Hang the carcass on a nail or hook by its right leg.
2. Remove the head and front feet, and let it bleed.
3. To skin the rabbit, cut off the tail and cut the fur from around the hind legs at the hock.
4. Slit the fur on the inside of the leg to the root of the tail.
5. Peel the pelt from both hind legs to the tail.
6. Then pull the pelt down off the body. Be careful not to get hair on the carcass.
7. Draw the skin inside out so that the fur is on the inside.
8. Stretch the rabbit skin before it dries out. You can make a stretcher from a piece of No. 9 gauge wire 60 inches long. Start at the middle of the wire and wrap the ends in opposite directions around a smooth 1½ or 2-inch pipe forming a 3 coil spring. Bend the ends so they are about 14 inches apart.
9. Pull the skin over a wire stretched with the front legs centered on one side between the arms of the stretcher.
10. Pull the skin as far as possible and fasten the skin of each hind leg to the arms of the stretcher with a clothespin.
11. Hang the skins to dry in a well ventilated place.
12. When they are completely dry, store them by wrapping in newspaper. Do not let two skins come in contact with each other.

Rabbit Meat

Procedure

Use the following procedure to dress a rabbit. You might like the recipe.

1. To dress the rabbit, use a sharp knife to cut around the anal opening and down the abdomen to the neck. Be careful not to puncture the entrails.
2. Split the chest and remove the entrails, but leave the liver.
3. Be sure to remove the gall bladder.
4. Cut off the hind legs at the hock joint.
5. Wash the carcass in cold water.
6. Let the carcass cool and then refrigerate.

Recipe

I would like to share an Old World recipe with you for stewed rabbit with prunes. It is a deliciously different way to prepare rabbit. Here it is straight from our kitchen to yours.

1. Clean, cut up and wash thoroughly one medium-sized rabbit.
2. Salt and pepper both sides of each piece.
3. Brown slightly 1/3 to 3/4 stick of butter in a roaster.
4. Place the rabbit pieces in the butter and brown well on both sides.
5. About 4 or 5 minutes before the second side is browned, cut up a medium-sized onion and allow it to saute until it is transparent.
6. When the onion is sauteed, add 1½ cups of water, 2 large buttons of garlic (sliced), salt and pepper to taste, and a very small pinch of leaf thyme.
7. Bake in a 350° oven for 1½ to 2 hours or until tender.
8. Approximately 45 minutes before the rabbit is done, add 8 or 10 prunes to the rabbit and allow it to finish cooking.
9. When done, remove the rabbit and prunes, and thicken **45** the gravy slightly with a mixture of flour and water. The prunes lend an ever-so-slight sweetness to the gravy.

Absolutely delicious!

Sanitation and Disease

Sanitation

You can do a good job of feeding and managing your rabbits, but if you don't carry out good sanitation practices, the program will not be satisfactory. Good sanitation takes time and must be accomplished on schedule if odors and diseased animals are to be prevented.

Hutches should be cleaned and disinfected on a regular schedule. The type of hutch you use will determine how much time it will take. Wire hutches require less time than wood hutches, or wood and wire hutches. An all-wire floor in any type of hutch is easier to maintain, since the manure and urine will fall through into catch pans or on the ground. The all-wire hutch is even better. All the droppings fall out, and there is no wood to absorb odors. The all-wire hutch makes disinfecting much easier also. A blow torch run over the hutch will do an excellent job.

All open waterers and feeders should be cleaned daily. Clean self-feeders and automatic waterers every week. Wash the nipples on the waterer with soap and disinfect them.

The nest box should be kept clean. It should be cleaned and disinfected (1) before the doe kindles, (2) when the young leave the nest, and (3) when the box is removed. Never kindle a new litter in a nesting box that a prior litter has used until the nesting box has been completely disinfected.

46

The manure and litter material should be removed from the rabbitry. The manure can be used for fertilizer in the garden, flowerbeds and lawn. It is an excellent source of plant food.

In the past few years, a number of rabbitries have combined their operations with that of raising fishing worms. Worm beds can be developed under the rabbit hutches. Worm beds reduce the odor, and at the same time produce an income. This works very well in the warmer climates. In very cold weather, the worms will burrow deep in the beds, and the manure will build up. This can be rectified by adding a covering of sawdust, peat moss, or vermiculite. This also aids in worm development.

Diseases

It is beyond the scope of this book to cover all the diseases, parasites, and illnesses, and their treatment. Diseases are caused by living organisms, such as viruses, bacteria and fungi. A combination of good sanitation, proper feeding and good care usually results in healthy animals that are not as susceptible as animals that have low resistance caused by poor feeding and lack of care. Crowding increases the possibility of diseases and parasites.

If a disease or illness develops, consult with a local breeder, or contact your state diagnostic service center. The local county agent can furnish the address and other pertinent information. If the herd is large enough to justify a veterinarian, call him at the first sign of trouble.

The Department of Agriculture has a publication, Commercial Rabbit Raising Handbook No. 309, that gives information on rabbit diseases and parasites.

Breeding

Breeding

As you gain experience in raising rabbits, improving the stock by judicious mating becomes more important. A great deal of satisfaction can be achieved when results approach the goal of the ideal. The subject of breeding is far too voluminous to try to set down in this book, but some basic information about breeding rabbits is in order.

Age

As a general rule, the meat-type does should be bred at 8 to 10 months of age. The young buck will attempt to mate at an earlier age, but this should be discouraged. If an underage buck serves the doe successfully, the young will probably be small and have more abnormalities. The development of the individual rabbit is just as important as age. Some develop to maturity more rapidly than others. Slow developing animals should be culled from the breeding stock. It is also important not to wait too long to mate the doe the first time. Does that are delayed in their first mating may require forced mating.

Schedule

48 The breeding schedule you follow will have to be determined by the type of production, the climate, your equipment and your time. Profitable operations strive to kindle at least 4 litters from each doe during the year. Based on a gestation period of approximately 31 days, plus 8 weeks nursing period, the 4 litters per year can be obtained provided no skips occur. If the size of the litter is very small, or if something happens to the litter, the doe can be bred right back earlier than the regular schedule. The condition of the doe should also be considered. If she is in poor condition after weaning her litter, give her a rest to regain good physical condition before being rebred.

Mating

The doe will indicate readiness for first mating by restlessness, nervousness, making efforts to join other rabbits, and rubbing her chin on the hutch. This condition may continue for some time, and as the doe has no regularly recurring heat period, the mating can take place at any time. Most breeders set up a regular schedule in order to eliminate the guesswork. Records are very important; separate cards should be kept on each doe and buck.

One buck for each 10 breeding does should be maintained for maximum results. Normally, the buck should be mated only once every 2 or 3 days.

The doe should always be taken to the buck's hutch for mating. The doe sometimes will reject the buck if he is placed in her hutch; she may even fight and injure him. Also, bucks are slow in performing in a strange hutch. When the doe is placed in the hutch with the buck, mating will probably occur immediately. If not, leave the doe and buck together for about 5 or 10 minutes. After the buck mounts and falls over on his side, mating should be accomplished. Then return the doe to her hutch. Don't leave the doe in the buck's hutch, since two mature rabbits will fight.

If the doe won't accept service, you will have to restrain her. To restrain a doe, use the right hand to hold the ears and a fold of skin over the shoulders. Place the left hand under the body and between the hind legs. Place the thumb on the right side of the vulva, the index finger on the left side and gently push the skin backward. This procedure throws the tail up over the doe's back. The weight of the body is supported by the left hand, and the rear quarters are elevated only to the normal height for service. Bucks become accustomed to this handling and will not normally object to such assistance. However, if the buck sniffs the hand and turns away, rub the doe's fur with your hands and try again. It is also a good idea to hold the doe in this manner when using a young buck for the first few times.

The average rabbit breeder should use a system of line breeding and periodically obtain new bucks to service his does, ones that are not closely related. In-breeding, the mating of closely related stock such as brother to sister, or father to daughter, should not be attempted until the breeder has gained considerable experience.

49

Pregnancy test

Most breeders use one of two methods to test for pregnancy. One method is to test mate by returning the doe to the buck's hutch after about 18 days. If, on being placed in the hutch, the doe avoids the buck, or if she growls, whines or fights, the doe is probably pregnant. All does that pull fur and attempt to make a nest 18 to 22 days after mating should be test mated.

The other method used by experienced breeders is to examine the doe 12 to 14 days after mating. Gently restrain the doe with one hand, and with the other cupped forward, feel the doe's abdomen. If the doe is pregnant, the young will feel like small marbles. Do not use very much pressure at this stage, as the unborn are easily damaged.

Gestation period

The gestation period, or the period from mating to kindling, is 31 or 32 days. There may be a few exceptions, but if the doe runs over more than a couple days, she should be culled from the breeding stock.

Occasionally a doe will mate, or be stimulated sexually and fail to become pregnant. This can happen if the buck is sterile at the time of mating, if the doe is kept in a hutch next to a buck, or if the doe is ridden by another doe. There is nothing that can be done when false pregnancy occurs. The period lasts for 17 days. Within 18 to 22 days, the doe will show signs of being ready to mate by pulling her fur and attempting to build a nest.

Do not handle the doe in the last few days of her pregnancy unless absolutely necessary. Open her hutch only to give her feed and water. She should not be disturbed by noise or action. Dogs and cats must be kept completely away from the doe. Enclose the area around the hutches to prevent intruders from getting close to the rabbit hutches.

Kindling

Completely disinfect the nest box about a week before kindling is expected. Put fresh, clean, soft straw, dry leaves, wood shavings or loose grass into the nest box to build the nest.

50 Immediately before the doe *kindles,* she will remove fur from her breast and line the nest with it. The doe will cover the young with this fur to protect them. The doe and her young should not be disturbed except to remove the dead young or adjust the nesting material. In about 2 weeks, remove half of the nesting material to make more room.

Young rabbits are born with their eyes closed. They will begin to open in about 10 days, and should be completely open in about 16 days. At this time the young will begin to leave the nest and eat with the doe; however, they will also continue to nurse.

Some does will destroy and eat their young. Cannibalism can

be caused by several factors. However, before condemning the doe, make sure that predators are not to blame. Rats and snakes will sometimes get into the hutches. Proper feeding and handling during pregnancy will do more to prevent this tendency than anything else. If the doe is guilty of cannibalism, she should be culled from the breeding stock.

Clean the nest box regularly after the young begin to come out and feed with the doe. When the entire litter comes out for feeding, remove the nest box unless the weather is very cold. Removing the nest box from the hutch will give the rabbits more room to move around.

To determine the sex of the rabbits at this age, open the aperture just in front of the anal opening by pressing with the thumb and forefinger. In young bucks the male organ will protrude slightly and form a round circle. In the doe, a slight depression with a slit will appear.

The young should be weaned at 8 weeks of age. If they are to be kept for breeding stock or grown to heavy weights for roasters or stewers, take them from the doe and put them in separate hutches. Separate the young does from the young bucks. The rabtits that are to be marketed should be ready at 8 weeks, and taken directly from the doe at that time. The doe will dry up in a few days and should be rebred at this time.

51

Record keeping

Keep a simple set of records on all breeding stock. The hutch card is very important if knowledge of the rabbit's performance is to be available for reference. Without knowledge of the individual performance of each rabbit, it is almost impossible to improve the operations and increase profits. These hutch cards can be obtained from the local feed dealers. A properly filled out hutch card will give the rabbit's identification number, the dates of mating, the dates of *kindling,* litter sizes, and litter weights at various dates before weaning. Put the hutch cards in a plastic bag and attach them to the hutch so that they will be available at all times. In addition, keep a performance book, one that contains all the information that is on the card, plus information on the animals' ancestry. By monitoring the outstanding individuals' records and selective mating, great improvement can be made in the breeding stock, thereby increasing profits.

Breeding stock is identified by tattooing a record number in the rabbit's ear. Tattooing instruments can be purchased from most livestock supply houses. To avoid being clawed, restrain the rabbits while they are being tattooed. An effective way to accomplish this is to build a box just large enough to hold the rabbits, leaving a hole in the top for the ears to stick through. The box should also have several small holes to provide ventilation, and the floor should be adjustable so the box can be adapted to various sizes of animals.

Breeds

The following breeds have proven to be the most popular in the United States.

American
A large white and blue rabbit. At maturity it will weigh 8 to 11 pounds. It is considered an excellent meat, fur and show animal.

Californian
A large white rabbit with black ears, feet, nose and tail. At maturity it will weigh 8 to 10½ pounds. The Californian was developed from crosses between the Himalayan and Chinchilla. This rabbit is very popular as a meat animal. The black on this animal does not deter fur buyers as it is removed in trimming.

Champagne d'Argent
Also known as French Silver. At birth the rabbit is black, but as it matures it turns to a silver or milk blue color. The fur is used in its natural color. The average mature weight is about 10 pounds, and it is a good meat producer.

Chinchilla
There are three types of Chinchillas being raised today — the Giant, the American, and the Standard. The Chinchilla is prized for its fur. The mature animals weigh from 9 to 12 pounds. The meat is considered average.

53

Checkered Giant
A predominately white rabbit with black or blue markings. The ideal mature weight is 12 to 14 pounds. The fur is highly desirable, and the meat is excellent.

Flemish
The largest of the standard breeds being raised today. Some mature bucks weigh as much as 20 to 22 pounds. The color is varied grey, white, blue, sand, or black. The meat is good, and because of its large size, it makes a very good show animal for 4H Club and FFA members.

New Zealand

There are three colors of New Zealand rabbits; reds, whites and blacks. They are the most widely raised breed in the United States, and although named New Zealand, they are American in origin. They are excellent meat animals, and the fur is in good demand. They are also widely used by research laboratories. The mature animals weigh from 8 to 12 pounds.

New Zealand

Siamese Satin

This is also another all American breed. The Siamese Satin makes a fine show rabbit. The pelt is in high demand, and the meat is considered very good. The mature weight is from 8 to 11 pounds.

54

Siamese Satin

CHICKENS

Raising chickens can be a most profitable operation for the country place provided you have space for the necessary facilities, and can oversee a flock without too much of an expenditure for labor. You can have two types of operations — one just large enough to provide eggs and/or meat for the family, or a commercial type operation designed to raise hundreds or thousands of birds.

If the flock is to consist of only a dozen or so hens and/or a few broilers raised for home consumption, the facilities required will be minimal; however, the need for proper feeding and care of

55

the birds will be the same as needed for profitable poultry management in large commercial operations.

If you decide to get involved in a commercial operation, you will have to decide which type of enterprise you want: egg production, broiler production (for meat), *breeder flocks,* or pullet growing. After you decide upon the particular operation, you will need to determine the facilities that will be required. Poultry houses are pretty much the same design, but the size is expanded to handle larger flocks. Also, you cannot keep birds of different ages in the same poultry house.

The poultry enterprise that most small farmers consider is egg production. Hens kept principally for egg production, if obtained from reliable *bred-to-lay stock,* can maintain a high rate of production throughout the entire year if they are properly managed.

Broilers raised for meat production require an intense effort. Commercial growers usually raise at least four flocks a year, marketing about 97% of the birds they start, and producing a pound of meat for every 2.4 pounds of feed consumed. To compete in this market, you must do a very efficient job.

You can compete and have a profitable poultry operation if you pay attention to management practices that eliminate waste and losses and consider the following.

1. Maintaining a large enough flock so that you use your labor economically. The size of the flock that is economical for you will be determined by how much time you and your family will have to devote to the project.
2. Producing a high-quality product, whether it be market eggs, hatching eggs or meat. A quality product is always the foundation upon which to build a successful business.
3. Starting with high quality birds.
4. Using good fresh feeds from a reliable source.
5. Keeping the poultry houses clean and dry.
6. Employing sound marketing practices and insuring that a suitable market exists for the product.
7. Providing adequate space and proper sanitation.
8. Watching for diseases and parasites.

Selecting the Stock

When you are ready to start your poultry operation, make sure you leave enough time for the planning stages. Pay attention to your local markets and think carefully about the ages of the birds you buy.

Egg Producers

Always purchase top quality, healthy birds that have been developed for a high production rate through the entire year. Good hens should average laying 250 eggs per year with proper management, and a high quality White Leghorn hen may lay as many as 300 eggs a year.

Market

Before you purchase the birds for your flock, check your local marketing outlets for their requirements. For example, some markets will not accept brown eggs, while others prefer them. In most sections of the United States, white eggs are preferred and sell for slightly more; however, in the New England states, brown eggs are preferred. It suffices to say that the breed chosen should produce the color and type (size) of egg preferred in the particular market to be served.

White Leghorn first generation strain crosses and crosses of inbred lines lay white eggs and are the most popular lightweight varieties for laying flocks because of their excellent productivity. The medium weight breeds usually lay brown eggs. Of this group, the New Hampshire, Plymouth Rock, Rhode Island Red and first generation crossbreds are the most popular breeds. These breeds are raised both for their good egg laying and good meat producing qualities.

Age

There are three different ages of birds you can select: chicks, started *pullets,* and ready-to-lay pullets. Select birds that can best be adapted to your production method, equipment, space location and other existing conditions. Purchase your birds from the hatchery closest to you that has birds with the traits you want. The fewer miles the birds have to travel, the fewer losses you will incur. It would be a good idea to consult with local poultrymen about their recommendations on reliable sources.

1. **Baby chicks.** Order chicks at least 4 weeks in advance from a hatchery or breeding farm. They will sell high quality, day old chicks for less that it costs to hatch them on the farm. The chicks will need heat and will have to be vaccinated, *dubbed* and *debeaked.*

Baby chicks are available as *straight-run* or as *sexed chicks.* Straight-run chicks are cheaper because they are boxed at random as they come from the incubator and will normally consist of 50% cockerels and 50% pullets. With the medium breeds, the *cockerels* can be raised for broilers; however, with the light breeds, the cockerels are poor meat types. The sexed chicks are sorted as they come from the incubator. Pullets cost more than twice as much as straight-run. The light weights cost more than the medium weights.

2. **Started pullets.** Order started pullets at least 3 months before they will be needed from a hatchery or breeding farm. These chickens, which have been brooded and no longer need supplemental heat, require less equipment and care than the day-old chicks. In addition, they normally will have been vaccinated, debeaked and sexed. The started pullets are usually between 6 and 8 weeks of age. When you buy started pullets, ask the grower about the strain or cross of the pullets, the type and number of vaccinations, history of any medications administered, and the kind of feed the birds have been eating. Do not make a radical change in the kind of feed they have been eating. It is also a good idea to determine if medication has been added to their drinking water. The higher cost of these birds reflects the additional cost involved in getting the baby chicks through the brooding phase.

3. **Ready-to-lay pullets.** Order these birds 6 months in advance from specialized pullet growers. They are sold when they are 16 to 20 weeks old and will begin to lay almost as soon as they are received. The grower should provide information relative to vaccinations, medication, rations, etc. The ready-to-lay pullets will cost more than other age groups of similar quality birds because they have been raised through the unproductive part of their lives.

Number

Don't overcrowd the available facilities when you determine the number of birds you need. Allowance should be made for normal losses from diseases, natural causes and culling. For each 100 hens desired in the laying flock, start with 220 day-old straight-run chicks, 110 sexed day-old pullets, or 105 six-week-old started pullets.

Meat Producers

Birds grown for meat production usually are crosses or hybrids. Cornish varieties are popular for use as the male parent because their chicks develop meaty breasts and legs. The varieties most often used for the female birds are strains with white plumage because they produce birds with excellent market appearance.

Market

Most birds raised for meat are marketed to poultry processing plants or to cooperatives. Some growers farm process their birds and market them locally to supermarkets, restaurants, or directly to the consumer. When this method is used, pay attention to all state and local laws and regulations governing such activity.

Top quality dressed or ready-to-cook birds can only be obtained from birds that are in prime condition at the time of slaughter. Do not feed the birds for 12 hours prior to slaughter, and give them plenty of water to flush them out during this time.

Exercise extreme care in handling birds being prepared for market in order to minimize losses from bruises, smothering and shrinkage. If they are to be delivered live, do not crowd them into delivery coops. Early morning delivery is best.

The production of capons is a specialized field and has a limited demand. Make a market survey before becoming involved in raising capons to insure that a market exists. The cockerels should be castrated when they are 3 to 5 weeks old. After the operation, keep the birds in a separate pen for 3 or 4 days. The birds will fatten faster, and the meat will be more tender if they are *caponized;* however, they require more feed and a longer period of time to reach marketing size.

Age

For meat production, almost all flocks are started from day old straight-run chicks. Breeders continually improve their stock to increase their growth rate, feed conversion ability and market appearance.

Most meat chickens are sold as broilers or fryers when they are 9 to 12 weeks old. Modern methods and improved rations have made it possible to raise chickens weighing 4 pounds or more at this age. It is possible to raise four crops of broilers and fryers a year.

Chickens kept until they are 4 to 6 months of age are sold as roasters. Since the female chickens of the age are kept as layers, most roasters are males. Capons are male chickens that have had their reproductive organs removed. They normally produce more meat than other chickens do.

Housing

The most extensively used housing system in meat production is the loose floor system. The pole type construction is widely used for facilities and is most satisfactory. More space should be provided if the birds are to be raised as capons or roasters. Lights are provided 24 hours a day for broiler production, with the usual lighting system requiring one 60 watt lamp for each 200 square feet of floor space.

Housing

Pole-type buildings are economical to build, maintain and clean. They are adapted to all types of flocks — replacement chicks, growing pullets, layers, breeders and meat-type birds. The building should meet the following criteria:

1. The floor should be easy to clean and disinfect.
2. Walls should be of a material that can be easily washed.
3. The building should have a ventilation system, built-in gravity systems and adjustable roof ridge ventilators. Electric fans are often provided where summer temperatures are normally high.
4. It should be vermin-proof.
5. It should have a piped-in water system, which is protected from freezing.
6. Electricity is essential in order that artificial lighting can be provided for a uniform light "day" in the poultry house, and to operate equipment.
7. It should have room for storing feed, equipment and eggs.
8. A dropping pit should be designed to hold droppings for several months. The top over the pit should be covered with 1 inch wire mesh. For ease of handling, it may be made of 6 ft. x 6 ft. panels. Feeders and waterers are often placed over the pit.

61

Egg Producers

The trend is toward total confinement in egg production with either the floor housing system (also litter or "loose" housing) or caged housing system being used.

Floor housing

Floor housing allows birds to move about freely on the floor of the poultry house, or inside pens that divide large floor areas into manageable units. This system may also be adapted to brooding, growing and maintaining any type of poultry flock. It is particularly suited for small flocks.

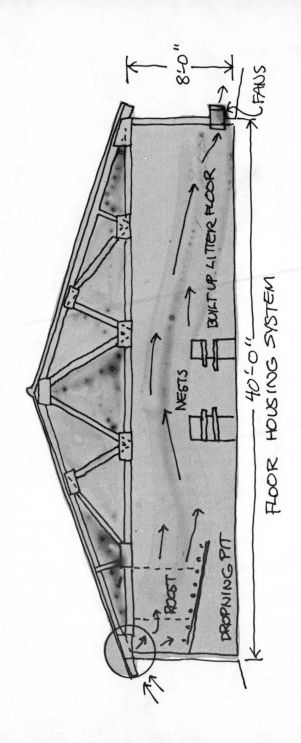

FANS

8'-0"

BUILT UP LITTER FLOOR

NESTS

FLOOR HOUSING SYSTEM

40'-0"

ROOST

DROPPING PIT

62

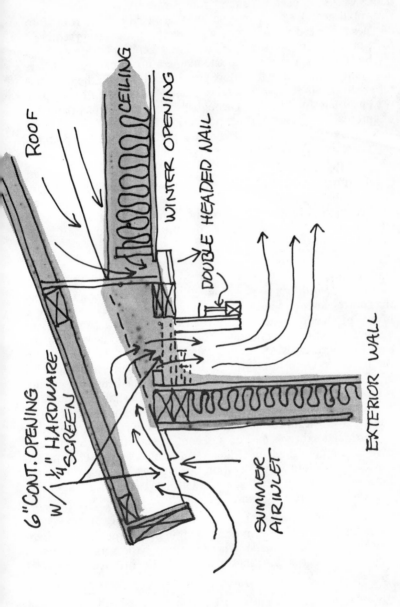

ROOF

CEILING

WINTER OPENING

DOUBLE HEADED NAIL

6" CONT. OPENING W/ 1/4" HARDWARE SCREEN

SUMMER AIRINLET

EXTERIOR WALL

63

Space requirements per bird in a floor system are the same as for all types of chicks up to 10 weeks old. In general, chicks less than 6 weeks old need 1/2 square foot per bird, chicks from 6 to 10 weeks old need 1 square foot per bird, growing pullets from 10 to 20 weeks old need 1½ to 2 square feet per bird, and layers require 2 to 3, or more, square feet per bird. The exact number depends on the body size of the bird and the temperature. Pullets and layers need about 1/2 square feet more space per bird when the temperature is above 80°F. As a general rule, large flocks require less space per bird than small flocks. Through efficient management and use of automatic equipment, some poultrymen have effectively reduced space requirements. When the space per layer is reduced, birds should be debeaked and more care is required.

The floor housing type of poultry house should provide clean, dry, comfortable housing for the birds throughout the year. An interior temperature range of 45°F. to 80°F. is satisfactory for good egg production. Moisture is a common problem in poultry houses, so fresh air should be circulated, but the house should be free of drafts.

Caged housing

Caged housing for egg production is now almost exclusively the controlled-environment type. The main objective of a structure in egg production is to modify the outside climate conditions to achieve maximum productivity from the layers. In the building design for caged birds, the major consideration should be to obtain the optimum temperature range. Layers are comfortable between 55°F. and 80°F. In cold weather, heat from the hens may be conserved in an insulated house and used to keep the house warm. Supplemental heat is generally not necessary if the house if fully insulated. Layers begin to show stress at temperatures above 80°F. — egg production begins to drop and continues to drop as higher temperatures are reached. In climates with persistent 90°F. temperatures and low humidities, evaporative cooling can be used advantageously. In winter months, a ventilation system is necessary to remove moisture from the building.

Cage size, type and number of birds per cage must be determined and the arrangement decided upon before the final layout of the building can be made. There are two basic arrangements of cages — the stair-step arrangement and the tier arrangement.

1. **The stair-step arrangement.** This arrangement does not utilize space as efficiently as placing cages directly above each other. Stair-step arrangements have generally been only partially

mechanized, with feeding and egg gathering usually done by hand. When the flock consists of 10,000 birds or more, it can become economically practical to mechanize the feeding and egg gathering operations. Dropping boards below upper deck stair-step cages are not necessary; thus the associated cleaning can be mechanized more easily.

2. **Tier-cage arrangement.** More birds can be housed in the same amount of space, but because dropping boards must be used under the upper tiers, manure handling is greatly increased. Most of the manure has to be removed by hand labor.

The width of the house is determined by cage row widths, number of cage rows, aisle width and the number of aisles. Houses with mechanical ventilation may be up to 40 feet wide for optimum air movement. The practical width limit for natural ventilation is 20 feet.

The lighting requirements in a caged house are different than they are in floor housing. Since the caged birds are closer to the lights than floor birds, use lower wattage bulbs that are close together. Light spacing should be no more than 1½ times the distance from the lower tier to the lights. Uniform light is desired, so place one row of lights between each row of cages at the aisle, and use reflectors on the lights.

In some locations cages may not be feasible as flies and excessive odor can be a problem when cages are used. The type of waste disposal system you use must be considered when you design the building.

Storage
Space must be provided for storing equipment, feed, eggs and manure.

1. **Equipment.** This can be stored in either the poultry house or a convenient separate building. It does not require any special features.

2. **Feed.** Feed needs to be centrally located to cut down on handling. Try to make your feed storage area completely rodent-free. Losses from rats and mice can be staggering. More feed dealers are delivering in the bulk. When it can be justified, consider bulk storage in metal bins. Two thousand layers is usually the cut-off figure on which to base the economic feasibility of using bulk storage. In determining how much storage space is required, figure that 100 Leghorns or other lightweight layers will eat about 25 pounds of feed a day, while the heavyweight breeds will eat about 30 pounds per day per 100 birds.

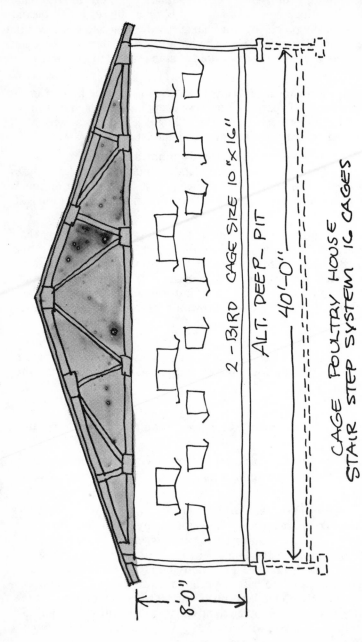

2-BIRD CAGE SIZE 10"×16"

ALT. DEEP-PIT

40'-0"

8'-0"

CAGE POULTRY HOUSE
STAIR STEP SYSTEM 16 CAGES

66

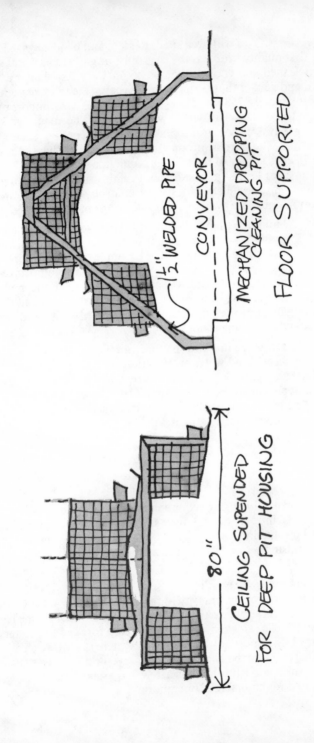

1½" WELDED PIPE

CONVEYOR

MECHANIZED DROPPING
CLEANING PIT

FLOOR SUPPORTED

80"

CEILING SUPENDED
FOR DEEP PIT HOUSING

3. **Eggs.** You will need space to store and handle eggs. To insure a first quality product, the eggs must be gathered several times a day, cleaned and cooled to 55°F. to 60°F. in less than a 6 hour period, and held at that temperature. Keeping the relative humidity at approximately 75% in the egg cool room is also important. If eggs are to be marketed twice a week, you will need enough space for four days' production, plus space for cooling each day's production. The normal production from each 100 hens would be about 75 eggs a day, so the storage requirements would be 75 x 4 x the number of layers (in hundreds). Prefabricated egg holding and cooling rooms, complete with proper controls, humidifiers and refrigeration units, are available in a wide range of sizes.

4. **Manure.** With maximum air drying, you can store manure in the dropping pit with minimum odor. Air movement over the surface of the stored manure should be ample to cause droppings to cone upward directly below the cage rows. The air movement should come from the outside under the eaves of the building, down across the cages and out at the lower walls. You can do this by placing most of the exhaust fans in the lower walls. Add circulation fans where drying is not adequate.

If you practice in-place manure storage, some biological degradation occurs, and water evaporation reduces the manure weight by over one-half. Average moisture content of stored manure should approximate 50% wet bulk. The bulk accumulation will be about one cubic foot per bird per year. Don't subject the dropping pit to any outside water sources.

Meat Producers

The general housing requirements for raising broilers seems to be either facilities for a very few, say a dozen or so, or for big commercial production involving 10,000 or so at a time. The days of the farmer raising a few broilers for market seem to be a thing of the past.

Housing for a small number

The most convenient way to raise a dozen or two for home use is with a battery cage system that includes a brooder as one level of the battery. The chicks are very easy to care for, and the battery can be stuck into almost any building where there is a little excess space. Electricity would be the only necessary utility. This system has shown such good results that a few large installations have been fabricated for commercial operations.

Housing for a large number

The big broiler production units, for the most part, consist of floor housing systems of the same general design as that used for layers, with the exception that brooders are used to start the chicks off. To give the chicks a proper start, the brooder must provide a temperature of about 95°F. in winter and 90°F. the rest of the year.

Some types of brooders heat the entire room, but with the increasing cost of fuel, this is giving way to the hover type that warms only the area under the hover, while the rest of the room remains relatively cool. Chicks will feather better when they have a cool place to exercise.

Chicks are usually started under unit brooders that have a capacity of from 500 to 1,000 chicks. The temperature under the brooders is reduced 5°F. a week to a minimum of 60°F. The hover should provide enough light to attract the chicks.

Space requirements for broilers are normally figured at about 1 square foot per bird. A normal size house is 40 feet x 250 feet, which is large enough to house 10,000 birds. Four broods of broilers are normally grown in one building each year.

Raising Chickens
for the Replacement Flock

In addition to the two general types of housing (floor housing and caged housing), chickens are rasied in different kinds of houses at different ages. Many farmers avoid the problem of handling chickens of different ages by always purchasing chickens at a particular age. However, if you decide to raise chickens from birth to death, the following information will be helpful to you.

The Brooder House

Brooding the chicks should be done in an environment that fosters normal, healthy, economical growth. The brooding of chicks for broiler production can and is carried out at all times of the year. The brooding schedule for chicks to be raised for replacement in the laying flock should be timed so that when egg production drops from the old hens, the new pullets are ready to lay. To achieve this smooth change in flocks, brooding must take place 5 to 5½ months before the replacements are needed. A 12 foot x 16 foot brooder house will accommodate about 200 chicks to 8 weeks.

Equipment

In selecting equipment to use in the poultry operation, make certain the equipment is safe for the birds, convenient to use, and above all, easy to clean. Use as much automatic equipment as possible. Mechanical feeders, waterers and pit cleaners can save hours of labor; however, the cost of purchasing such equipment will need to be balanced off against available labor and its cost.

1. **Temperature.** To give day-old chicks a proper start, the brooder must provide a temperature of about 95°F. in the winter, and 90°F. the rest of the year. The chicks need enough space under the brooder so that they can keep warm without being crowded. Chicks will pile up trying to keep warm, and some will be smothered to death. Space under the brooder should average about 6 square inches for each chick.

2. **Fuel.** Electric and gas brooders are usually the best because they can be easily regulated, are easy to clean, and are more

dependable. However, it may be necessary to supply heat to the entire building if extremely cold weather is encountered during the brooding season. A recent design of a brooder house uses solar energy to heat water that is circulated in pipes encased in the concrete floor. It has a storage tank that stores the hot water for use when the sun does not shine. There is a water heater for standby. The chicks raised in the brooder did very well, and the cost of operation was reduced.

3. **Light.** A small 7½ or 15 watt light should be used for the first couple of weeks to attract the young chicks to the hover.

4. **Feeders.** The hanging-type tube feeders have just about replaced the trough type where automatic feeders are not used. The hanging tube feeders require less labor and provide more eating room. The chicks do not get bruised as easily and the old feed is eaten first because the hopper is filled from the top. The feeders can be raised as the chicks grow, and to make cleaning easier. For each 100 chicks allow 3 hanging feeders 15 inches in diameter with a 25 pound capacity. There are several types of automatic feeders available. Select and install them in accordance with the manufacturer's directions. Add feeding space in hot weather to prevent the chicks from bunching up.

5. **Waterers.** Use two one gallon water fountains for each 100 chicks during the first two weeks. Then, provide hanging or automatic fountains with 40 linear inches of trough space per 100 birds at three weeks, and 50 linear inches at seven weeks. If the float type is used, check float operation daily to insure that it is working properly.

6. **Litter.** The litter can be any absorbent material that reduces the moisture in the poultry house and serves as an insulating material in cold weather. Do not use old litter left over from a previous flock of chicks as the risk of disease is too great for the savings involved. However, the litter can be built up by adding small thin layers on top of the new litter as needed. During cold weather, litter may reach a total depth of 6 or 8 inches; not as much litter is required in warm weather.

71

The litter should be clean and dry — but not dusty when installed. Litter can be made from corn cobs, peanut shells, wood shavings, saw dust or other similar materials found around the farm. Commercial litter is available made from peat moss, cane fiber and cottonseed hulls.

Place the litter on a dry, clean floor, with the first application of 2 or 3 inches placed 2 to 3 days prior to receiving the chicks. Keep the litter as dry as possible, and stir it occasionally to keep it from packing. As wet spots develop, remove and replace with dry, new litter. If the litter continues to be wet, apply 10 to 15 pounds of hydrated lime per 100 feet of floor space and stir.

Preparing the brooder house

The brooder house should be prepared several days in advance with the following items properly taken care of.

1. Clean and disinfect the house thoroughly including the brooder, feeders, waterers and all other equipment.
2. Check the ventilation system, the electrical service, water lines, and drains. After the chicks are in the brooders is a poor time to have to make repairs.
3. Place fresh litter.
4. Each brooder should be properly placed and be in operation, and all thermostats should be working properly.

Start the brooder a couple of days before the chicks arrive. Set the temperature at about 95°F. in cold weather and 90°F. in warmer weather. Follow the manufacturer's recommendation for reducing the temperature and for all other operations. Normally, the temperature is reduced about 5°F. weekly until it reaches 75°F.

Caring for the birds

Place the chicks under the *hovers* as soon as they arrive. The chicks' actions provide a good guide to their temperature. Chicks crowd together near heat when they are too cold, and they pant and gasp (often at the outer edge of the hover guard) when overheated. Check the temperature twice a day during the first week. Take the temperature about 3 inches from the floor and about 3 inches inside the outer edge of the hover.

A guard to help keep the chicks under the heat can be made from cardboard boxes. Place the guard 2 feet from the edge of the hover. Move the guard farther away from the heat each day, and remove it completely after a week.

72

Provide heat until the birds are well feathered. Don't remove the heat too soon, because the birds might develop respiratory problems. Do not crowd the chicks. They may pile up or smother if they do not have enough space or if they become frightened. In summer operations, protect the birds against temperatures above 95°F.

Cannibalism is often a problem with birds raised in confinement. It usually can be prevented or controlled by debeaking. Toe picking may be the first sign of cannibalism. Remove injured chicks from the rest of the flock, and treat their injury with a stop-pick preparation. Allow the injury to heal completely before returning the chick to the rest of the flock.

Debeaking may be done at any age. It is a good idea to order the chicks debeaked at the hatchery. Debeaking does not harm the birds or reduce their vigor.

Effective vaccines have been developed for four major respiratory diseases — Newcastle disease, bronchitis, fowlpox and laryngotracheites. Vaccination of the flock should be based on the needs of the individual flock, and on local conditions. Have all vaccinations completed by the 16th week; otherwise it may delay egg production. Give all vaccines in strict accordance with the manufacturer's recommendations.

The Growing House for Started Pullets

Chickens are ready to move to the growing house as started pullets when they are 6 to 8 weeks of age. If you purchase chickens at this age, the following information is also applicable.

Large pole-type houses are widely used for rearing pullets. A standard 36 foot x 140 foot poultry house will accommodate 3300 pullets. Confinement takes less land and less labor than range-rearing systems. Confined birds also have fewer losses from *coccidiosis,* worms and other parasites, and from such natural enemies as hawks, crows, foxes, skunks and dogs. The house should be about 2 or 3 times larger than the brooder house.

Pullet growing for egg production requires basically the same facilities and management as for broiler production, except the birds must be grown to maturity. If the pullets for egg production will be housed in a caged system later, they should be put in cages in the growing house.

73

If they will be housed in a loose housing or floor system later, they should become accustomed to roosts. The roosts are normally made of 2 x 4's or 2 x 6's, depending on the distance to be spanned, with the top edges beveled. Light breeds will require about 8 inches of roost space, and medium-sized birds 10 inches of roost space. Build the roosts on a slant with the back 24 inches higher than the front. Place the slats about 15 inches apart. The roost should also be built over the dropping pit. Design the dropping pit to hold droppings for at least 6 months. Include in the pit area enough space for the waterers and the feeders.

The Laying House

The laying house is where the mature hens lay their eggs. Either the cage system or the loose flooring system is appropriate, with the latter being especially suitable for a small flock. The cage system is best in the warmer climates; however, layers can be housed in cages in other areas if the house is well insulated and the ventilation is controlled. The house needs to be filled to capacity so the body heat from the hens will provide heat to keep a minimum temperature range of 40° to 55°F. The caged system is not always desirable if flies and odor can cause a problem in heavily populated areas. A standard 36 foot x 140 foot poultry house will accommodate 2,500 layers.

Equipment

1. **Light.** Lights are necessary in order to achieve the best egg production. The lights should be on a time clock, with automatic dimming devices to simulate evening twilight and morning daybreak. For daytime, morning, or evening lighting, use 60-watt incandescent lightbulbs with shallow-dome reflectors. Supply one fixture for each 200 square feet of floor space. Place all wiring in the poultry house in conduit, and cover all outlets, such as convenience receptacles.

2. **Feeders.** Allow six hanging feeders 15 inches in diameter for each 100 hens. Locate the feeders within 10 feet of the waterers.

3. **Waterers.** The waterers should provide 18 linear feet for each 100 layers. In hot weather, increase the space by one-fourth. Place the waterers over the dropping pits to minimize the amount of wet litter in the laying house.

If you use an automatic watering system, it will require approximately 8 gallons of water per day for each 100 layers. It is a good idea to have a standby water supply for emergency use in case the automatic system fails to function. Lack of water for even a short period of time can play havoc with egg production. A couple of 55 gallon drums filled with clean water should make a satisfactory standby supply.

4. **Nests.** If the hens are not caged, they will need nests. Well-designed nests can reduce the time needed to gather the eggs, and prevent losses due to breakage. Nests are usually made from metal or wood. Individual nests just large enough for one hen should be 10 to 12 inches wide, 12 to 14 inches high, and about 12 inches deep. A perch below the nest will help keep the nest clean and reduce egg breakage. Supply one nest for each four hens. Community type nests will accommodate several hens at the same time. A nest 2

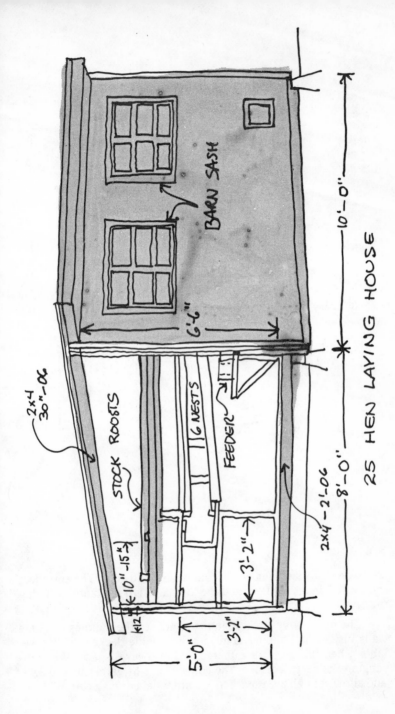

25 HEN LAYING HOUSE

10'-0"

8'-0"

6'-6"

BARN SASH

2x4 30"-OC

STOCK ROOSTS

16 NESTS

FEEDER

2x4 — 2'-OC

10"–15"

K12"

5'-0"

3'-2"

3'-2"

75

2 HENS
PER CAGE

feet wide by 14 feet long will accommodate 140 hens. The entrances should be 8 inches square, and the top hinged to facilitate gathering the eggs.

The nests may be placed in the middle of the building or along walls inside the building, and may be double decked. This saves labor when the eggs are gathered and also saves space. When arranging the nests, consider the convenience of gathering the eggs, and allow enough aisle space to accommodate a small cart.

Preparing the laying house

1. Clean and disinfect the house and install new litter in preparation for the pullets. This will usually prevent the carryover of diseases and parasites from the old birds to the pullets. Leave the laying house empty for at least one week if possible. During this period, inspect the house thoroughly, and make all needed repairs. The less the pullets are disturbed after they are moved in, the better.

2. Check and clean the feeders and waterers. Be sure to remove all old feed that might have been left in the feeders and dispose of it.

3. Clean the nests, burn all old nest materials, and install new nesting material, made from wood shavings, peanut shells, rice or oat hulls, sawdust, or one of the commercial products. There is always some egg breakage in the nests, but if this happens too often, it probably is not the nesting materials at fault, but rather that the hens are not receiving enough calcium in their diet. Installing the nests in the laying house before the pullets are brought in will help to cut down on floor eggs.

Caring for the birds

As the pullets are moved to the laying house, examine each one individually. Any that appear to be unthrifty, deformed or weak should be removed. Proper culling is essential for a profitable laying flock, and culling should be a continuing process throughout the year. Identify and remove unproductive birds as they can be the principal reason for reduced profits. Culling the laying flock is usually based on a combination of factors including (1) egg laying indicators, (2) bleaching of pigments, (3) molting, (4) diseases and (5) body conformation. The local county agent can furnish additional information on guides to culling the farm flock. Culling poultry is a skill that has to be developed.

You should manage your laying flock so that as egg production drops to an unprofitable level at the end of the flock's first laying year, the old hens can be removed from the house, and, ideally, the pullets for replacement have started to lay at about 10% production. The egg laying rates of the old hens and their planned replacement with the pullets should determine the time that the laying house is emptied and prepared for the new flock.

Under normal conditions, it is not economical to carry hens through the molt at the end of their first year. The hens will eat 6 to 7 pounds of feed during the 2 or 3 months they are out of production. However, it may be profitable to carry high producers through the second year if (1) egg prices are high, (2) the birds are healthy and vigorous, (3) separate housing is available, (4) the flock is carefully culled to eliminate all but the very best producers, and (5) special precautions are taken to prevent the spread of diseases to the new layers.

Range Rearing a Flock

Range rearing large flocks is not very well adapted to the country place; however, small flocks can be range-reared and they do benefit from the exercise, sunlight and green feeds. Range may be used for pullets from the time they are brooders until they are ready for the laying house. When the pullets are moved from the range to the laying house, they should be debeaked and treated for parasites and other stress-producing proclivities.

Birds on range may eat 5 to 15 percent less mash and grain than confined birds. As mentioned, parasites and predators on range must be controlled, and clean range is required to avoid outbreaks of diseases. Clean range can be maintained by using a 2 or 3 year range rotation program. At the end of the pullet growing season when the birds have been removed, plant the range to crops or pasture grasses. Do not use manure from the other poultry houses for fertilizing the range.

One acre of good range can support 300 to 500 growing pullets. Allow the birds to run freely. Do not crowd the range, and do not mix birds of different ages on the same range. Cannibalism is not normally a problem with range birds, and the birds should not be debeaked unless they start showing signs of cannibalism.

Shade is a requirement for birds on range. Place water and feed in the shade. Put drinking fountains about 15 feet from the feed and evenly spaced. A range shelter usually consists of a small, portable building with wire walls and a wire floor. Move the shelter as often as necessary to prevent the location from becoming highly contaminated with droppings, or the grass from being killed. To prevent losses from predators, lock the flock in the shelter in the evening and release early in the morning.

Feeding

Feeding the poultry flock is a critical part of poultry management. The poultry feed should provide all the necessary proteins, carbohydrates, fats, minerals, vitamins and added growth factors in the proper balance. Incomplete or unbalanced rations often are the cause of nutritional diseases. The feed formulas used by the commercial manufacturers are balanced rations specially formulated for the age and type of chicks. Mixing poultry feed on the farm is not an economical practice. If a custom mixing facility is available where you can combine the necessary concentrates with home-grown grains, you may reduce feed costs slightly. When buying feed, consider the formula, the reputation of the feed itself, the company that manufactures it, and the cost.

In addition to regular ground mash, feed is available as pellets and *crumbles.* Processing pellets and crumbles increases their cost, but also increases palatability and reduces feed waste. Some medications (which help prevent diseases and speed growth) are included in feed. When you use a medicated feed, follow the manufacturer's directions exactly, and be sure the withdrawal period is met before marketing.

Keep water before the birds at all times. If you add medication to the water, be sure to follow the manufacturer's recommendations carefully. Provide at least 1½ gallons per day for each 100 chicks up to 3 weeks of age. Increase the supply to 3 gallons per day until the birds reach 6 weeks of age, then 6 to 8 gallons per day per 100 birds. Provide additional water when temperatures are above 80°F. For example, at temperatures above this level, 100 layers require 9 to 10 gallons of water each day.

To maintain healthy profitable birds, keep fresh feed available at all times. Do not overfill the feeders — about 2/3 full is recommended. This will help to prevent waste and insure fresher feed. For efficient feeding, keep the lip of hanging feeders at the level of the birds' backs. Fill non-automatic trough feeders in the early morning, and again during the day whenever the feed gets low. If leftover feed is not clean and palatable, remove it before refilling the feeders. Never put moldy or contaminated feed in feeders.

A drop in feed intake is an early sign of trouble, including disease outbreak, molt and stress, or a management problem such as poor ventilation, overheating or an abrupt change in schedule. Correct the cause as quickly as possible. If you don't know the cause, call in a poultry specialist.

Feeding Chicks

Always buy complete starter feeds for baby chicks. The starter ration contains 20 per cent protein, the muscle-building nutrient. Give the chicks starter feed until they are 6 weeks old.

Allow 40 pounds of starter ration per 100 baby chicks for the first 2 weeks, and 250 to 300 pounds per 100 birds from 2 to 6 weeks. Meat-type birds require more than the light breeds normally used as layers.

Provide feed and water as soon as the birds are put in the brooder. Cardboard boxes, such as the shipping crates the chicks came in, can be cut down and mash spread over them to make temporary feeders. If you use hanging feeders, set them on the floor for about 5 days, and raise the feeders and the pan gradually. The chicks will learn to use the feeders and waterers by the time they are 2 weeks old. If you use automatic feeders make the change gradually.

Feeding Pullets

When the chicks are 6 weeks old, change from the starter ration to a growing ration. The complete growing ration will contain about 16% protein. If grain is to be fed with the growing ration, the growing ration should contain 20% to 22% protein. Corn, wheat, barley, oats, millet, grain sorghum or combinations of these may be used.

Begin with 10 pounds of grain for each 100 pounds of mash, and gradually increase the grain until the birds are eating equal parts of grain and mash. Put the grain and mash in separate feeders. When pullets reach 18 to 20 weeks, gradually replace the growing mash with laying mash over a period of two weeks.

Feeding Layers

If the layers are to be fed a complete mash ration, it should contain about 15% protein. If grain is to be fed in equal parts, the mash should be a 20-22% protein ration. Unless you raise the grain yourself, you probably won't find grain feeding profitable.

Laying hens have high calcium requirements, because egg shells are largely calcium carbonate. Therefore, have grit available at all times for birds that are fed grain. Oyster shells or limestone grits are suitable.

Some feed manufacturers prepare a complete feed that includes all the necessary minerals, vitamins and nutrients. The best ration for layers is the one that will produce a dozen high quality eggs at the least feed cost.

The hen needs high quality feed to reach and maintain her maximum egg laying capacity. Feed consumption per bird varies primarily with egg production and body size. On the average, 100 lightweight layers will eat 25 pounds of feed per day. The medium weight layers will eat 2 or 3 pounds more per day per 100 birds.

Feeding the Breeding Flock

Feeding the breeding flock is more expensive because breeding mash is required; therefore, use breeding mash only when the eggs are to be used by a hatchery. Start feeding the mash about one month before the eggs are to be saved for hatching. Breeders require larger amounts of vitamins and minerals in the right proportions to give high hatchability and develop good chicks. Feed the breeding flock in the same manner as layers, although the ration differs.

Feeding Meat Producers

The birds raised for meat production are fed special rations prepared to give the maximum amount of meat per pound of feed consumed. Broilers are produced on a ration of 2¼ pounds of feed for each pound of meat. The manufacturer's directions should always be followed to achieve the best results.

Marketing Eggs

Most farmers of small acreage sell their eggs in their immediate areas. Some make contracts with local supermarkets, with restaurants or other large users of eggs. Most producers, however, sell wholesale to produce dealers, cooperatives, shippers and egg cracking companies. Some farmers establish consumer routes and sell directly to the consumer; others have roadside stands. The direct selling usually brings higher prices and generates more profit. However, if you have to hire labor to process and sell eggs, retail operations may not be profitable.

The consumer wants high quality eggs. A bad egg will almost assuredly "turn off" a customer. Strive to market eggs with the fresh-laid appearance and with flavor and nutritive value. The shell should be strong, regular and clean; the white should be clear and firm; and the yolk light colored, well centered and free from blood spots.

The egg characteristics are inherited. Bred-to-lay birds have been produced through careful breeding programs that develop desirable egg traits, as well as sustained laying ability. The kind of feed the layers are fed affects quality of the eggs, as do insufficient minerals and vitamins. Do not allow roosters in the laying flock unless the eggs are to be used for hatching chicks.

The eggs should be gathered twice a day, 3 times or more in hot weather, and kept clean. Eggs are perishable, and they deteriorate rapidly without proper care. Gather the eggs in open baskets so that air will circulate around them, and store them in a cooler where the temperature is between 45°F. and 55°F. Because humidity also affects egg quality, hold it at 70%. Eggs will absorb odors, so don't store them near such items as onions, kerosene, or other items with pungent odors.

Never wash clean eggs; however, dirty eggs may be washed or buffed before they are graded and packaged. Most eggs that are sold direct to consumers are packed in cardboard or plastic cartons containing 2 rows of 6 eggs each. Most eggs that are sold to wholesalers are packed in crates containing 30 dozen. Eggs should always be packed with the large end up. This maintains the egg in its normal physical balance.

The eggs should be candled and graded in accordance with the grade standards established by the U.S. Department of Agriculture. The eggs should also meet all the requirements, including licensing, of the state in which they are produced.

You might want to consider producing hatching eggs for a hatchery. Before beginning a hatching-egg flock, however, make a definite agreement with a reliable hatchery. The hatchery will usually pay a premium price for the eggs, but they in turn will set standards for breeding, sanitation, disease control, and egg handling for their supply flocks. The hatchery will supervise the flocks that supply them, and in most cases, control the blood lines of the flock; sometimes they will even furnish the breeding stock themselves.

Breeding flocks are managed much the same as regular laying flocks that are floor raised and loose housed as layers. In addition to the hens in the house, cockerels will be required in a ratio of 6 to 100 for lightweight breeds, and 8 to 100 for heavyweight breeds. The birds must be mated at least two weeks prior to saving the eggs for hatching.

Hatching eggs should be gathered several times a day, and in extremely hot or cold weather, they should be gathered every hour.

Disease

Prevention is the most satisfactory way to deal with poultry diseases, parasites and pests. Many disease conditions can be prevented through good management, but cannot be cured once they actually occur. The following are effective preventive measures:

1. Keep the poultry house locked.
2. Limit visitors. If a visitor must enter a poultry house, have rubber boots available for him to wear.
3. Use a vaccination program developed for your area.
4. Obtain only "clean" chicks that are certified pullorum and typhoid free.
5. Supply sufficient amounts of clean, fresh water and feed.
6. Do not let trash and waste accumulate around the poultry house.
7. Control rodents.
7. Do not allow wild birds to enter the poultry house. Screen and plug all openings.
9. Locate houses a minimum of 50 feet apart.
10. Keep feed delivery trucks as far away from poultry houses as possible.

If a disease outbreak does occur, determine the cause as quickly as possible. If necessary, send 4 or 5 live chickens to the nearest poultry diagnostic laboratory, together with all pertinent information such as the number of birds affected, number of deaths, feeding program, vaccines used, and the source from which the birds were obtained.

Chickens that obviously are sick should be destroyed and burned. Separate birds you intend to treat and keep them as far away from the other birds as possible. Treat them as suggested by the poultry laboratory. The location of the nearest poultry laboratory can be obtained from the local county agent.

Mites, lice and ticks are common external parasites that occur in poultry. The use of one or more of the following methods will normally provide control:

1. Paint the roosts with a 3% malathion emulsion. Use one pint for each 150 feet of roosts.
2. Treat the floor litter with a 4% or 5% malathion dust. Use 1 pound to cover 50 to 60 square feet.
3. Spray the entire house with 1% malathion spray or 0.25% coumaphos spray.
4. Spray the chickens with a 0.25% coumaphos spray or 0.5% Rabon spray. Use 1 gallon to treat 100 birds.
5. Treat the birds individually with a 4% malathion dust. Use 1 pound of dust to treat 100 birds.

Rats and mice should be controlled in the poultry house area. They eat, contaminate and waste feed, carry diseases and insects, and kill chicks. They often go unnoticed because the losses are gradual, and they are seldom seen when a person enters a poultry house.

The best way to fight rats and mice is to get rid of their hiding places, which means clearing out trash dumps, piles of lumber, manure piles and garbage heaps. Find and block their runs or burrows; then use poison. Information on rat poisons and uses can be obtained from the Publication Unit of the Bureau of Fish and Wildlife Service, U.S. Department of Interior, Washington, D.C., 20240. Ask for Wildlife Leaflet #402, Anticoagulant Rodenticides for Control of Rats and Mice.

Breeds and Breeding

The five standard breeds described here are the most popular breeds used in commercial operations. Hybrid strains are also extensively used. They are the result of inbreeding and crossbreeding to obtain a specific superior type of bird, either for meat or egg laying ability.

You will need to take into account your personal preferences, certain local conditions, economic production requirements and consumer preferences when you select the variety you want to raise. A personal preference for a variety, strain or cross to work with will add to one's personal satisfaction. Some will choose standard varieties; others will select crossbreeds or inbreds, although these hybridized commercial birds are not really breeds of chickens.

There are dozens of classic breeds which are not listed here, including the Wyandotte, a classic American bird, which is a good layer and has tender, tasty meat (named after the Wyandotte Indian tribe of the St. Lawrence Valley). The Dorking and the Orpington are English breeds that are large, good eating and lay fairly well.

If you plan to raise chickens more for the pleasure of the task without any special concern about "production," you might want to play a modest part in restoring the classic breeds. This can be done through experimentation, by trial and error, or by obtaining expert advice from the Society for Preservation of Poultry Antiquities at Owatonna, Minnesota.

Plymouth Rock

Origin: Connecticut, USA

Maturity: Fairly early. Egg production starts at 5½ to 7 months of age.

Plumage Color: One variety is barred, with each feather crossed by light and dark bars of approximately the same width. Other varieties are white.

Meat: Very good; popular on all markets.

Egg Production: Good. Shell color ranges from light to medium brown.

Weight: Females 5½ to 7½ pounds; males 8 to 9½ pounds.

The barred Plymouth Rock, which was one of the first breeds and varieties to be developed in America, is named after the sturdy rock on which the Pilgrims landed. For many years it was the most popular of all varieties. For body shape, the White Plymouth Rock usually excels the barred variety.

Plymouth Rock

New Hampshire

Origin: New Hampshire, USA.

Maturity: Early in most strains. Egg production starts at 5 to 7 months of age.

Plumage Color: Light to rich chestnut red, except black in the tail, male are a brilliant deep chestnut red, while those on the female are medium chestnut red.

Meat: Good. Most strains make excellent broilers and fryers.

Egg Production: Generally good, depending on the strain. Shell color is dark brown, and eggs are large.

Weight: Females 5 to 7 pounds; males 7 to 9 pounds.

The New Hampshire was developed in New England primarily from a foundation of Rhode Island Reds. Continual selection of breeding stock for rapid feathering, rapid growth, large brown eggs, and strength and vigor brought about this comparatively new breed of chickens. The New Hampshire is used extensively in crossbreeding with other chickens, for both broiler and egg production.

New Hampshire

Rhode Island Red

Origin: Rhode Island, USA
Maturity: Fairly early. Egg production starts at 6 to 7½ months of age.
Plumage Color: May vary from bay to rich red, except some of the tail and flight feathers are black.
Meat: Good. Cockerels make excellent capons.
Egg Production: Good. Shell color ranges from brown to dark brown.
Weight: Females 5 to 7 pounds; males 7 to 9 pounds.

Rhode Island Reds were bred for many years in a small community near Little Compton, Rhode Island, before they were introduced to the rest of the country. Their vigor, productivity and attractive color appealed to poultry growers. Thus their popularity spread rapidly, and for many years they were the leading variety of medium weight breeds in the United States. The young grow rapidly; however, some strains are still slow feathering.

Rhode Island Red

White Leghorn

Origin: Italy
Maturity: Early. Egg production starts at 5 to 6 months of age.
Plumage Color: White in all sections.
Meat: Only fair in the young; poor in adults.
Egg Production: Excellent. Shell color white.
Weight: Females 4 to 5 pounds; males 5 to 6½ pounds.

The true exhibition-type Leghorn is one of relatively small size with refined features. When in full plumage it presents beautiful curves in all sections. As the demand for egg production was emphasized, the larger, more rugged type was developed. The single comb White Leghorn is easily the most popular of all the recognized varieties. The single comb White Leghorn is used extensively for crossbreeding to obtain hybrids with good egg laying ability. The breed is usually vigorous, and is looked upon with favor by hatcherymen because of the high fertility and hatchability of its eggs and the livability of the chicks.

White Leghorn

Black Australorp

Origin: Australia.
Maturity: Fairly early. Egg production starts 6 to 7½ months of age.
Plumage Color: Black, or greenish black in all sections.
Meat: Fair. Dark shanks may be an objectionable factor.
Egg Production: Generally good. Shell color light brown.
Weight: Females 5 to 7 pounds; males 7 to 9 pounds.

The Australorp was developed by the Australians using the Orpington as the foundation stock. They developed this breed through a period of continual selection, principally for egg production. It never gained much prominence in the United States until it was discovered that the Australorp male and the White Leghorn female produced a very satisfactory crossbreed.

Inbreeding and Crossbreeding

Inbreeding consists of mating together closely related birds. The inbreeding is carried on for at least three successive generations of full brother-sister matings of individuals from promising families. Inbreeding intensifies all hereditary characteristics so that the desirable ones may be carried on and the undesirable ones discarded. For commercial purposes, one inbred line may be crossed with other inbred lines. Chickens produced in this manner have increased greatly in popularity in recent years. Such birds can be expected to give a good performance because the undesirable traits are weeded out and hybridization restores vigor. The high level of selection alone should be responsible for improved performance.

Crossbreeding is commonly defined as the mating of birds belonging to different breeds or varieties. In recent years, crossbreeding has become fairly common. Crossbreeding tends to improve hatchability of eggs, viability of chicks, rate of growth and egg production. Some poultrymen have developed strains of high egg producers and broilers by practices involving inbred lines and crossbred lines to obtain the hybrid vigor. It is important to note that all crossbreds are not superior to all purebreds. It is true that if good breeders are used, there is a tendency for the offspring to be slightly superior to the parent stock.

Glossary

Artificial insemination
The impregnation of a female with the male semen (usually collected and frozen for later use) using a mechanical device.

Bred-to-lay stock
Birds that have an ancestry of high egg production.

Breeder stock
A flock kept to produce fertile eggs, especially for hatching.

Broiler
A young chicken grown to 2½ pounds dressed weight for the market.

Brooder house
A specially built chicken house to start the baby chicks in.

Brooder
A heated hover to start the baby chicks under until they develop their feathers to keep them warm.

Caged housing system
A method of housing laying hens in small cages with 1 to 5 hens per cage inside a large sheltered area.

Caponize
To remove the testes from the male chicken.

Capon
The castrated male chicken.

Coccidiosis
A serious pulmonary disease of chickens.

Cockerels
Young male chickens.

Concentrates
Feed that is very high in protein content.

Conversion efficiency
The rate at which a bird or animal can convert feed to meat.

Cooling boxes
Small wire cages that young rabbits are kept in during the day, especially during hot weather.

Crumbles
A method of preparing feed that is not as fine as mash and not as large as pellets.

Cull
To remove unproductive chickens from the flock or herd.
Debeak
To cut back the top part of the chicken's beak.
Dropping boards
Trays or boards that are placed under the cages or roosting areas to make cleaning easier.
Dry does
Female rabbits that are not nursing young.
Dub
To have the comb and wattles trimmed on chickens.
Egg cracking companies
Companies that buy eggs when they are abundant and cheap and process them into dried eggs or canned eggs for use by bakeries.
Feed intake capacity
The amount of feed an animal consumes daily when given free choice.
Floor housing system
A system in which chickens are allowed to move about freely on the floor.
Ground mash
Feed that is milled so that it will pass through a fine mesh screen.
Growing house
A shelter that chicks are moved into when they have completed feathering and no longer require brooder heat.
Hocks
The back of the knee joint of the hind legs.
Hover
A canopy on a brooder to hold the heat around the baby chicks.
Kindles
When a doe rabbit bears her young.
Kindling
The act of a doe rabbit giving birth to her young.
Lactation
That period of time in which females produce a milk flow.
Laying flock
A flock of hens kept for egg production only.
Laying house
A shelter for housing laying hens.
Nesting box
A special enclosure for the doe rabbit to use for kindling.
Pullet
A young hen less than one year old.
Range rearing
The practice of raising chickens on the ground in yards or pastures.

Ready-to-lay pullets
Chickens that have been grown to the stage at which they are ready to start to lay.

Ruminants
Animals that graze grass, chew a cud and have a complex 3- or 4-chambered stomach.

Started pullets
Young female chicks that are feathered and are ready to go to a growing house.

Starter ration
A specially prepared mash that is high in protein and used for the first few weeks.

Starting stock
The foundation stock to begin a herd or flock.

Straight-run chicks
Unsexed chicks that are grouped for sale as they are hatched.

Tether
To restrain with a rope or chain so that animals are forced to graze in certain areas.

Tilting squeeze chute
A special device that not only restrains the animal but will also allow the animal to lay over on its side. This is very useful for trimming the hooves of animals.

Countryside Gardening Books
Little Book Series
5½ by 8 inch format

INDOOR ASSORTMENT

Cactus & Succulents (101)
Herb Gardening (102)
Foliage Houseplants (103)
Flowering Houseplants (104)
Vines & Ivy (106)
Ferns & Palms (107)
African Violets (108)
Orchids (111)
Houseplant Handcrafts (114)
Houseplant Multiplying (117)
Don't Throw it Away . . . Plant it (118)
Houseplant RX (119)
Greenhouse Gardening (126)

OUTDOOR ASSORTMENT

Container Planting (105)
Geraniums (109)
Begonias (110)
Garden Bulbs (112)
Correct Planting Methods (113)
Vegetable Gardening (115)
Entice Birds to Your Garden (116)
Shade Trees (120)
Evergreens (121)
Groundcovers, Vines & Hedges (122)
Annuals & Perennials (123)
Better Lawns (124)
Rose Handbook (125)

Large Books
8¼ by 10½ inch format

SIX WAYS TO GROW HOUSEPLANTS, (201)
    by Muriel Orans, 265 color photos, **$3.95**
NEW IDEAS IN FLOWER GARDENING, (202)
    by Derek Fell, 225 color photos, **$3.95**
LOOK, MOM, IT'S GROWING, (203)
    by Ed Fink, illustrated children's book, **$2.95**
HOUSEPLANTS AND INDOOR LANDSCAPING, (204)
    by Muriel Orans, 248 color photos, **$3.95**
HOW TO PLANT A VEGETABLE GARDEN, (205)
    by Derek Fell, 100 color photos, **$3.95**
HOME LANDSCAPING, (206)
    over 500 color photos, **$5.95**
BONSAI AND THE JAPANESE GARDEN, (207)
    by Domoto & Kay, 85 color photos, **$3.95**
RAISE VEGETABLES, FRUITS & HERBS IN CONTAINERS, (208)
    by "Doc" & Katy Abraham, **$2.95**

95

Countryside
Books

A. B. Morse Co.
200 James St., Barrington, Ill. 60010